WRITI[N]

FOR NUR[SES]
AND ALLIED PR[O]

FOR MY DAUGHTERS
JILLIAN AND SUSAN

WRITING
FOR NURSING
AND ALLIED PROFESSIONS

Desmond F.S. Cormack
PhD, RGN, DipEd, MPhil, RMN, DipN
Reader in Nursing
Department of Life Sciences
Dundee College of Technology

BLACKWELL
SCIENTIFIC PUBLICATIONS
Oxford London Edinburgh
Boston Palo Alto Melbourne

© 1984 by
Blackwell Scientific Publications
Editorial offices:
Osney Mead, Oxford OX2 OEL
8 John Street, London
WC1N 2ES
9 Forrest Road, Edinburgh
EH1 2QH
52 Beacon Street, Boston
Massachusetts 02108, USA
706 Cowper Street, Palo Alto
California 94301, USA
99 Barry Street, Carlton
Victoria 3053, Australia

First published 1984

Set by Colset Pte Ltd,
Singapore
Printed and bound in
Great Britain by
Biddles Ltd,
Guildford and King's Lynn

DISTRIBUTORS

USA
  Blackwell Mosby Book
  Distributors
  11830 Westline Industrial
  Drive
  St Louis, Missouri 63141

Canada
  Blackwell Mosby Book
  Distributors
  120 Melford Drive,
  Scarborough
  Ontario M1B 2X4

Australia
  Blackwell Scientific Book
  Distributors
  31 Advantage Road, Highett
  Victoria 3190

British Library
Cataloguing in Publication Data

Cormack, Desmond F.S.
  Writing for nursing and allied
  professions.
  1. Nursing——Authorship
  2. English Language—Rhetoric
  I. Title
  808'.042'024613   RT24

  ISBN 0-632-01129-7

Contents

Prologue

An important feature of any profession is the extent to which the members contribute to the development of its literature. Many professionals, and nurses are no exception, need help in preparing to write for examination purposes or for publication. This text is directed to those who wish to write for publication, *and* to those who are seeking to maximise writing skill in essay-type exams and coursework. Throughout, you are reminded of the need to obtain and study the requirements, instructions or marking criteria of those for whom the work is being prepared.

Although the examples used in, and orientation of, this book are *nursing*, it has a relevance to other health care professions, and to non-health care professionals. Because the principles of good writing technique, structure and presentation are virtually the same, irrespective of your professional background, non-nurses may also find the book meets their needs.

For the sake of convenience, the term *nurses* is used in this book to include *all* nurses, midwives, health visitors and others with a nursing background.

Apart from the Recommended Reading list at the end of this text, no references to previously published works are included. You should note that the word *Example* is used for illustrations to avoid a confusion of terms.

Because of the uniqueness of every writer's style, it would be wrong to view this book as a model of writing style, the style used in this text is *my* style. Rather, the purpose is to discuss a number of techniques which will maximise your writing presentation, structure and readability. In short, it will help you develop a *personal* style.

Another purpose of the book is to present and discuss the many publishing opportunities which are available to members of the professions, and how to utilise these. I firmly believe that nurses and others are capable of writing for publication, are motivated to do so and have something important to write about. The 'block' for many, is a lack of information about the mechanics of writing and of how to get excellent ideas on paper and subsequently published.

None of the chapters can be fully utilised without some reference to a number of others. For example, in relation to 'Articles' or 'Coursework and Examinations' useful material will also be found in chapters entitled 'Writing Style Development', 'Illustrations' and 'References'.

Chapter 1
Writing Opportunities

The development of writing skills can present a formidable, yet rewarding, challenge to all professionals including nurses. Because of my nursing background, the examples used and the major orientation of this book relates to nursing. Very little of what is presented here, however, relates exclusively to nursing, and other professionals, particularly those with a health-care background, will find the material applicable to them.

Nurses are no strangers to writing, most spend a considerable amount of time in writing clinical reports on patients for example. However, such material is for a relatively limited readership with which the writer has close contact. Should the reader of an individual patient's report require further information or explanation, invariably access to the writer of that report from whom further information can be obtained is possible. The written information will be only a small part of the total information which is available. For example if a reader is informed that 'Mr Jones is to be discharged from hospital tomorrow', he/she will have considerable additional background knowledge of the context of that particular report.

In this book the phrase *writing skill* refers to a type of writing and writing skill with which most nurses have less day to day experience, it relates to writing longer pieces of work, often for publication. Although many will have had the opportunity to develop writing skills during training, to fulfil coursework requirements for example, this experience is limited from two viewpoints. First, the skills are frequently learned by nurses in training using a process of trial and error. It is extremely rare for nurses to be given a formal training in writing, something we do require to produce examination and coursework materials of a professional standard. Second, once we complete our training, we may well fail to develop our skills. This is not meant to imply that nurses are unable to develop these; as was mentioned before most write clinical report type material daily. Rather, it is being suggested that many have difficulty in writing longer pieces of material designed to be read by an audience with whom there is little personal contact. This problem is one which is experienced by many groups of nurses in various settings. During a writing workshop, presented by me and attended by nurse teachers, clinicians and students, it quickly became apparent that all groups had difficulty in demonstrating a high level of writing skill. This applied to nurses with considerable experience, as well as to nurses with much less experience.

In recent years nurses and other professionals have become much more aware of the increasing expectation that they should contribute more fully to the professional literature, that is that we become more involved in writing for publication. The purpose of this book is to convince *all* nurses that they have an important part to play in contributing to the professional literature. It is also intended to provide a number of practical guidelines, and some practical examples, of how to develop the ability and confidence to write.

A few decades ago the need to write, particularly for publication purposes, was much less apparent than it is today. The extent to which professionals in other parts of the world or country wished to, or required to, know of professional practice and events in other areas was rather limited. However, because of the explosion in professional information and knowledge in recent years, the written word is increasingly being used as a means of communicating with others. This means of communication is already well developed amongst some professional groups. Although medicine is the best known example, nursing is fast catching up as it develops its own expertise and experience of written information exchange. As nursing establishes itself as a profession, it requires to fulfil its writing obligations.

REVIEW OF WRITING OPPORTUNITIES

All nurses at all phases in their career are potential contributors to the nursing literature. Not all of this literature will be published, some being written for examination purposes, other materials being prepared for publication. Thus, nurses at every level of experience require to develop their writing skills fully. In relation to the learner nurse, such skills need not be confined to coursework and examination work. Whilst a beginner may have less to add to the nursing literature in clinical practice, he/she will have much of importance to say with regard to what it is like being a beginner in nursing for example. The learner is in a better position to comment on some aspects of nursing than the more experienced member of the profession.

The following review of writing opportunities, although not completely comprehensive, is intended to illustrate that there are a range of activities in which you may become involved. They are not presented in any order of importance or in the order in which you might get involved in them. For example you may well become an editorial panel member having never written a book, book review or journal article. Remember, few individuals will become involved in all aspects of writing, even during a life time within the nursing profession. Those who wish to write should choose the outlet which is most suited to their talent, experiences and aspirations. What is often the case is that a small measure of success will cause you to aspire to greater things. This is to be applauded and may well result in gaining the confidence to utilise writing skills more fully.

Although some help can be given to the beginner, there is no recipe which can ensure success, there is no easy route to producing high quality written material. While some have a natural talent for producing work which reflects an excellent understanding of their native language, most people have to struggle during the early phases of developing this skill. However, these skills can be learned and all professional nurses must be convinced of two things. First, all nurses can achieve success if sufficiently motivated, interested and willing to invest some time in writing practice. Second, all have something unique and important to contribute to the nursing literature. Such contributions may take a number of forms including: coursework and examinations; dissertations and theses; research reports; articles; books; publishing consultancies; and book reviewing.

Coursework and examinations

Two types of written work, coursework and exams, are similar in that they are both submitted for examination purposes. Thus, they will each be submitted to a readership with which you have some direct or indirect personal contact, the examiner. In general, this similarity holds good although the length, depth and quality of the piece of work may vary considerably. The work may vary from a three-page exam answer submitted by a first-year student nurse, to a thirty-page piece of coursework submitted by a postgraduate student.

In both instances the student has made the decision to undertake the course of study for which the coursework or examination answer is a requirement. Although this requirement may form a much larger part of one course, and a relatively small part of another, they are of equal importance in that the written work must be successfully completed to achieve success in the course generally. It is my experience that many nurses have relatively little difficulty in producing, say, one or two written pages (about 200–400 words). However, the prospect of writing a much longer piece is a cause for considerable concern for many, this problem being more apparent than real, and one which can be minimised with appropriate guidance and practice.

Dissertations and theses

The movement of sections of nurse education into higher education establishments has dramatically increased the frequency with which we have to produce dissertations and theses. These may be a requirement for diploma courses, graduate courses or courses for higher degrees. In my own teaching experience, I have assisted a number of nurses to produce a dissertation with an optimum length of 15,000 words. Almost none of these nurses had written anything exceeding three or four pages in length in their previous professional career, and all had grave reservations at the beginning of their course about their ability to produce this type of work. However, with appropriate guidance and supervision they produced high quality material, the same would be almost certainly true for other nurses who lack writing experience.

The ability to handle longer, rather than shorter, pieces of written work is becoming an increasingly necessary feature of professional nurse development. Many postbasic educational, clinical and administrative courses now have a firm component which requires the extensive use of these skills. Thus, the development of such skills can no longer be seen as an optional extra only for those who wish to publish. All who wish to participate in the available continuing education opportunities must be able to express themselves clearly and effectively using the written word.

The writing opportunities which I discuss may be 'optional'

in that a nurse may well proceed through an illustrious career without making use of them. However, bearing in mind the essentiality of published literature to the development of this profession, there will be greater expectation of all nurses to participate in the development of their literature. Other professional groups, very correctly, place considerable value on the efforts of their members for contributing to the literature. This applies to practitioners, academics, researchers and administrators alike. There can be no doubt that these expectations will become commonplace in nursing.

Research reports

As the current explosion in research among the various health care professions, including nursing, continues to develop, the ability to produce well-written readable research reports becomes more evident. Although a minority of nurses undertake, and therefore write about, research, the quality of the report has implications for the entire profession. A long-standing criticism of much of the existing research is that it is rarely read, far less implemented. Undoubtedly, the poor quality of many reports in structure, presentation and readability contributes to the infrequency with which they have been read and understood.

Although the prime responsiblity for decisions regarding the unique content of the research report will lie with the researcher and supervisors, the structure and presentation may be similar to other reports. It is often true to say that a 'blueprint' exists for presenting and structuring research reports, each report only requiring modifications in the style used. Chapter 9, 'Research Reports', deals with the questions of presentation, structure and style.

Articles

Preparing an article for publication in a professional journal may be the first type of publishing in which you will become involved. The number of articles required for publication has escalated dramatically since the 1970s, due in large part to the growth in the numbers of professional journals. To survive, each journal must attract an appropriate quantity and quality of articles. Bearing in mind that many of these journals are published weekly or monthly, the total number of professional articles published in a given year is considerable.

Some years ago the majority of nursing articles published in Great Britain and other countries were written by a minority of nurses who produced many articles each. This is no longer the case, writing material for publication in article form is no longer the domain of a few writers. It is now usual to see an article produced by a nurse in training, a first-year staff nurse or some other relatively inexperienced person.

There is a myth relating to publishing articles which needs to be exploded. It is that most journals are so overwhelmed by articles submitted for publication that it is almost impossible for even very experienced writers to have their articles accepted. It is my belief, providing a good idea is well-written and well-presented in the format required by an individual journal, that getting an article published is not as difficult as many imagine. It is surprising how many nurses who have never submitted or prepared an article for publication, labour under the illusion that having an article accepted is virtually impossible. The reality of the situation, in my view, is that lack of writing skill practice is the major problem in writing and publishing an article. In short the average nurse *is* sufficiently motivated and knowledgeable to publish; what is required is help in understanding the 'mechanics' of writing and publishing.

Books

Until recently, many books used by nurses, including those relating to nursing care, were written by non-nurses, a contribution for which this profession must be grateful. Although most of these non-nurse authors were medical staff, other professionals such as psychologists and physiologists wrote books used by nursing staff. Now the majority of texts used by nurses are written by nurses. There is still a need for nurses to use books which have been written by non-nurse specialists. However, there is an increasing realisation that we can, ourselves, contribute more fully to extending the range and quality of texts which we use.

Although nursing textbooks are often written by more experienced nurse authors, there is no reason why less experienced writers should not seek the opportunity to contribute to multi-author texts by, for example, writing a chapter on a subject which is within their area of expertise. Many books are now written by a number of authors, a multi-authored book, or are compiled and edited by one person, the general editor, who seeks chapter contributions from a number of other individuals. Beginner writers who have the appropriate skill and experience may be contacted by a general editor who wishes to organise a book. Again, there is no reason why potential contributors should not contact the general editor or the publisher and make it known that they would be willing to write a chapter on a specific topic. Nursing book publishers are interested to hear from potential authors, whether that person is able to write an entire book or contribute to one. If a publisher were contacted by sufficient number of individuals who, for example, felt able to write various parts of a book on surgical nursing, the publisher may well put these individuals in touch with each other with a view to preparing a book on that subject.

Publishing consultancies

Some of the publishing companies who have a special interest in producing nursing texts have no qualified nurse on their staff, others employ one or more nurse/editors. Both sometimes seek additional advice from individuals with the expertise appropriate to a particular text, proposed text or book outline. The advantage of this type of arrangement is that the company has access to a very large range of experiences and expertise. If the material relates to community psychiatric nursing, then a community psychiatric nursing expert can be contacted for assistance. Similarly, if the proposed material relates to health visiting then a health visitor expert can be contacted. This arrangement means that a wide range of nursing personnel contribute to the development of nursing literature in book form.

Although many, if not all, nursing journals will have qualified nurses on their staff, they can clearly not employ nursing staff with every conceivable range of skill and expertise. For this reason, as with book publishers, most journals utilise the services of nursing staff on a part-time basis which may be either paid or unpaid. For example, a journal may well have an editorial panel of nurses from a range of backgrounds, their function will be to help in the development of general publishing strategies for the journal and to look at individual manuscripts which have been submitted.

A journal may also appoint a number of referees who will be sent submitted articles for detailed examination. The referee will then decide whether the article should be accepted unchanged or, as is frequently the case, whether it should be sent back to the writer for appropriate changes to be made. As with publishing consultancies this involvement in the work of nursing journals allows considerable numbers of nurse practitioners, administrators, researchers and educators to be involved in the work and development of the nursing journal.

Book reviewing

As with articles and the journals which contain them, the number of new nursing texts appearing on the market has increased manyfold since the 1970s. This, accompanied by the increasing cost of texts, necessitates the development of a good professional book-reviewing system which will help the potential buyers decide which books to purchase and which not to purchase. This service is of vital importance to the nursing profession, to the authors of books and to those companies which publish professional nursing texts. It is clearly necessary to those who stock and organise nursing libraries and to individuals who purchase texts. A book-reviewing service is also of use to nurse teachers and nurse learners, and of considerable use to qualified nurses who may wish to maintain a small personal library throughout the duration of their career. Books are important to the individual, important to the organisation within which the individual works and, perhaps, most important, to the nursing profession generally.

A reviewing service is often one of these aspects of a nursing journal which is taken for granted. The reader of the review may well fail to give any consideration to the process by which a book is reviewed, and the review published.

Book reviewing, in common with all aspects of writing, requires special skills which can be learned. Also, book reviewing is within the scope of the average nurse who has developed an appropriate level of the writing skill, and who has an appropriate professional experience which enables him/her to make an informed comment on the contents of books.

There are a number of other types of professional writing which will not be dealt with in this text. These include writing letters to journals and the provision of news items to them. Both types of writing form a growing part of the literature. They have the distinct advantage of being much more up-to-date than either articles or books; both are often the only real source of certain types of information.

Recently a student of mine examined the content of one major British nursing journal over a five-year period; he was looking for written information relating to the subject of his research. Although he found virtually no information in the articles within the journal, he found the news items, editorials and letters to be an extremely rich source of information relating to the subject. Whilst the abstracting journals, nursing indexes and other similar services supply the researcher with easy access to published articles, the editorials, news items and letters in professional journals are usually not included in these systems.

Before discussing each of these writing opportunities in detail a number of other aspects of the writing process will be discussed. The materials contained in the next five chapters are central to a full development of writing skills.

EXERCISE

The exercise, which can either be used on a personal basis or as part of a writing-workshop programme, is designed to help you develop three essential skills: first, the skills which relate to writing itself; second, writing within a prespecified time frame-work; and third, using a predetermined number of words to express a specific view or point.

EXERCISE 1

Write a 400-word essay using free-flowing prose. The subject of the essay is 'Why I chose this profession'. The time available for writing the essay is 1 hour.

The essay should now be critically reviewed to see if it meets with the predetermined length and subject area. It should then be written in a second, or indeed a third, draft to meet a standard with which you are satisfied. Ask a friend to read your essay and give you an honest and constructive opinion on it.

Chapter 2
Who Should Write,
Why, Where and When?

WHO SHOULD WRITE?

All professional nurses, and those in training, require to use writing skills at some point in their career. For many, this skill unfortunately begins and ends during nurse training. With few exceptions, writing skills are acquired by the learner nurse in an accidental and incidental fashion. Large amounts of coursework require to be written in essay form and in many countries exams are written in essay form, and little attention is paid to development of these skills in learner nurses. Perhaps, it is assumed that these skills are a feature of all individuals who have recently left school. This assumption is wrong on two counts: first, many school leavers do not possess a level of writing skill which is required by the nursing profession and second, many learner nurses left school a number of years earlier and may be more than a little 'rusty'.

Exams and coursework apart, all professional nurses have an obligation to continue to contribute to the professional literature throughout their career. Unless this professional obligation is taken seriously, much of our professional literature will continue to be produced by the minority who have taken it upon themselves to develop these skills. There can be no excuse for a profession which is numerically dominated by clinicians and practitioners to have its professional literature created largely by a minority of researchers, academics and administrators or by those in related professions. Clinicians, researchers, administrators, teachers and learners each have a specialist contribution to make to the nursing literature. It is not the elitist activity it used to be, and is increasingly being contributed to by all levels of expertise within the profession.

It has been my observation that the more experienced a nurse is, the less confident he/she may be about contributing to the literature. This feeling commonly exists and results in a loss of shared knowledge and experience to others less experienced. Conversely younger nurses have much more confidence, but obviously have much less experience. Perhaps the nursing profession generally must share much of the responsibility for the present position which has resulted in a minority of its members writing for publication. It might be argued that we should expect our individual members to write, and should regard *all* nurses as having a duty to contribute to the literature upon which the development of nursing as a profession is to be based. Writing is not only for 'them' it is also for *us*. This expectation forms an integral part of other professional groups, medicine for example.

Nurses with writing experience clearly have a duty to nurture those skills in less experienced writers. They could and should be passed on during nurse training using essays and other forms of coursework as the basis for developing them. There is no doubt that such exercises would improve the coursework and essay writing of nurses during training. They would also go far towards encouraging nurses to continue to write after training ceases. Although nurse teachers are in an ideal position to develop these traits in learners, many nurse teachers themselves may have difficulties in writing. If this is so, then urgent remedial action requires to be taken whereby a suitable level of skill is achieved by all those who teach nurses. Thus, nurse teachers and others who come into contact with nurse learners will be in an excellent position to act as role models.

Those who have achieved some measure of success in writing for publication have a clear duty to help others to gain some experience. One way in which the experienced writer can help is by encouraging others to co-author an article or book chapter. Clearly this would involve giving all those involved in the publication equal credit for it. If the new, or junior, author has done the bulk of the work for the publication then that person should become the senior author.

Beginners often assume that nobody would be interested in what they have to say, some because they lack a string of academic qualifications. This view must be regarded as a myth, the majority of nurses internationally have no such long list of academic qualifications. All professional nurses with experience, with something to say, and the ability to write clearly and readably should write for publication.

Others may feel that they 'just don't have the time' to get involved in writing, being much too involved in *doing* the job of nursing to find the time to tell others about it. This view may be acceptable in the short term in that it allows you to devote all your time and energy to taking care of patients, teaching, administration or whatever. However, in the long term this view does a disservice to the nursing profession in that it prevents the dissemination of your valuable knowledge.

Although writing undoubtedly offers some personal rewards such as the sense of achievement resulting from having an item published, the major rewards are much greater than the personal ones. These come from a sense of having contributed to the wider development of nursing as a profession. Additionally, the financial rewards from a well-prepared and popular text can be considerable.

Thus, all professional nurses have a duty and obligation to become involved in writing. All professional nurses from all specialist disciplines and areas of expertise also have such a duty. All professional nurses during all phases of their professional career have a similar duty. Although this view is intentionally uncompromising, it is recognised that developing these skills poses some difficulties for a number of individuals. The purpose of this book is to minimise these difficulties and help you make the best possible use of the writing skills you undoubtedly have.

WHY WRITE?

All nurses will have experience of writing to pass examination hurdles. The importance of this type of writing is not to be underestimated, all nurses having achieved some success in this area. It should also be remembered that those who do achieve success, and pass the appropriate exams and coursework, may well do so in spite of, rather than because of, the help which is given in nursing schools relating to writing.

A small number of professional nurses become involved in writing as part of a work commitment. This may take the form of project work for personal use, or as projects commissioned by individuals further up the nursing hierarchy.

A further purpose of writing might be in relation to post-basic nursing. The level of this type of work will range from projects such as those undertaken as part of a first-line or middle-line management course to dissertation work undertaken as part of a college or university diploma. In some instances nurses will write a thesis as part of a requirement for obtaining a higher degree.

Perhaps the greatest potential for writing lies in the opportunities which we have to contribute to the professional literature. Let us consider the reasons why professional nurses should contribute to that literature.

To inform

There is a definite need for us to inform others of how we undertake nursing. The 'how I do it' type of writing may be based purely on personal experience or opinion, or may have a research base. All nurses are urged to examine closely their professional activities and ask the question 'Do I do or know something which may be of value to others?'

To educate

Nurse education is divided into two distinct areas: the school of nursing and the work place. For many years we have known that the material taught to nurses in schools of nursing does not quite match the reality of what occurs in the work place. Part of this situation stems from many nursing textbooks having been written by nurse teachers, academics and administrators, the groups who have least direct clinical contact with patients. It is vital that nurse clinicians play a much greater part in contributing to the literature upon which nurse training is based, and that they add to the contribution of those who are not presently working as clinicians.

To speculate and predict

Nursing is a conservative profession which, in the past, has done little to encourage those individuals who see the future and development of nursing in a way which is 'different' from the majority. Such individuals are sometimes branded as radicals or deviants. Although the encouragement of speculation and prediction results in a certain amount of uncertainty, we must become more tolerant of those willing to speculate and predict. They must be encouraged to share and publicise their thinking through writing and subsequent publication.

To question and challenge

The obvious ability of individuals to question and challenge subjects and decisions relating to their profession must be a healthy sign. There can be no doubt that every single individual professional nurse has the right, and should feel obliged seriously, to challenge all individuals or groups who make public pronouncements about nursing. This type of writing frequently takes the form of published interviews, letters to, or news items in, professional journals.

To raise issues

One way of highlighting important issues in nursing, and to cause large numbers of individuals to focus their attention on them, is to do so by writing for publication. All nurses have the right, the experience and the duty to raise issues for public debate. Such issues may range from 'the need for continuing education for nurses' to 'the extent to which senior nurse managers do or do not facilitate nursing research'. In the past the discussion of many such issues, and the proposed solutions, have been left to committees, nursing academics and high-ranking nursing administrators. These individuals and groups, although constituting an important part of the nursing profession, would not claim to have a monopoly in the discussion of relevant issues or proposing solutions.

Once such issues are raised by individuals, others have an obligation to contribute to the public debate. Clearly, the development of an appropriate level of writing skill will enable us all to present a much stronger and more reasoned argument.

To influence opinion

Although the opinion of individuals and groups is often shaped by personal experience, other factors play a part in influencing it. The written word is a powerful means of influencing opinion. A well-presented and forceful argument, which is either published or sent to an individual or group, can play a large part in helping them to understand the views of the writer. It is interesting to note that many more 'open letters' published by the nursing press are designed deliberately to influence all or a specific group of the readership.

To clarify your own ideas

When developing a new idea in some aspect of nursing, the individual is likely to publish that idea and, thereby, expose it to the critical view of a peer group. In this case, the purpose of the writing is to share your idea with others and to expect a 'feedback' from them and thus better understand, clarify and justify the ideas or proposals contained in the published material.

WHERE TO WRITE?

The opportunities for writing are numerous and are broader than many nurses realise. Some of the major outlets for writing are discussed in this book, others such as newspapers, popular journals and non-nursing publications are only referred to briefly.

In nursing and its allied professions, the largest source of original written materials is undoubtedly the hundreds of journals. While most of these journals relate to nursing in general, there is almost certainly a journal somewhere which deals with the most specialised aspect of nursing.

We have much to contribute to the non-nursing publication, either non-nursing health care related publications or 'lay' publications. Examples of the latter are popular magazines and newspapers. Nurses have a poor track record in contributing to non-nursing publications, compared with doctors of medicine who frequently write for non-medical publications. When nurses do publish for a non-nursing health care staff readership, they have a great deal to teach non-nurses about nursing. We frequently make the mistake of assuming that other professionals, doctors and physiotherapists for example, know as much about nursing as we know about medicine and physiotherapy. Not so, even though all groups should have a good understanding of each other's role. Are these other professional groups reluctant to allow nurses to publish in their journals? I rather think that the journals of other professionals rarely carry articles written by nurses because so very few of us *offer* material to them.

Another aspect of the nursing literature is that so little of it is of an 'international' nature. With a few notable exceptions, most journals publish materials which have been written almost exclusively by nurses residing in the country where the journal is published. We need to become more aware of the internationalisation of nursing, and that nurses in any given part of the world have much to teach, and learn from, nurses elsewhere. Although this position is changing, there is still a long way to go before we catch up with other similar professional groups. In considering how to make best use of writing skills, therefore, we must seriously consider the international nursing literature as a potential outlet. Providing that such material is relevant to groups outwith the country of its origin, we should make a vigorous attempt to have it exposed to as wide a readership as possible.

The uses to which writing skills can be put are large; there is clearly a multitude of possible outlets for the product of such skills. Those which have not been mentioned thus far, but which are of equal importance, include the preparation and submission of written evidence to committees, groups or individuals who are involved in nursing affairs. The written word can also be a persuasive tool in conveying your feelings to nurses and others who hold public office, members of Parliament for example. Remember, we are the most authoritative and best-informed spokespersons for nursing.

WHEN TO WRITE?

Ideally, all nurses should consider writing to be something to be undertaken during their entire career. It would be easy to say that the best time to write is 'when you have something to say', however this is not entirely true. All too often the reason given for failure to contribute to the nursing literature is that we cannot readily think of something about which to write. I think that all professional nurses can find, if they put their minds to it, something in their background, knowledge or experience which needs to be related to others in the profession through the written word.

Even if you cannot identify something about which to write at present, the possibility of writing in the future must always be borne in mind. For example, if you are about to embark on some new type of project or approach to nursing care, consider recording the progress of the project in such a way that it will lend itself to publication in due course. In short, the possibility of publishing in the future should always be regarded as a real one. Similarly, if you write dissertations or other forms of coursework as part of a course requirement, you should seriously consider whether the material ought to be reshaped or rewritten for publication.

Some potential writers will struggle for long periods with an idea in an attempt to write about it, often unsuccessfully. This will often be accompanied by the mistaken notion that perfection has to be achieved on the first attempt. Nothing can be further from the truth and, with a small number of exceptions, the written material may well go into three or more drafts before a final product is obtained. The point here is, do not wait for inspiration which you hope will result in instant perfection, just start and write *now*. Once a start to writing is made it is surprising how the material can be added to, refined and shaped into a desirable end product.

PERMISSION TO WRITE

At the time of deciding when to write, comes decisions regarding who to inform, consult or ask permission of. Although there are no straightforward answers to these questions there are some general principles which may be of value in avoiding a number of potential pitfalls. Whilst published materials no longer *automatically* carry a footnote in which the author thanks the hospital matron and consultant with whom he/she works, it is still necessary to give some thought to who should be consulted and informed. Although some nurse managers may regard the writing activities of their junior colleagues as being their own business, most still like to be kept informed of the publishing activities of junior staff.

As a general rule a private and personal opinion which is expressed in writing, and contains no reference to your place of work, does not require permission to be published. If, however, the written material does make reference to your place of work or relates to activities which are being undertaken in a specific work area, then the permission of the employing authority, requested via the nursing management structure, should be sought. Thus, if you are using material which relates to or is obtained from your place of work then permission must be obtained. Similarly if you are incorporating any material or ideas obtained from colleagues, then this must be formally acknowledged and permission obtained. In general it is probably best for most nurses in most circumstances to err on the safe side and at least consult, if not inform, senior nursing colleagues about the activities to be undertaken.

For some groups, such as those working directly for government departments, it may be essential that the employer's permission be obtained prior to any publishing activity. If in doubt, ask whether or not you need formal permission to publish. If permission is required, ensure that it is given in writing.

If consultation or informing procedures are not to be used, then you must make sure that the material presented is totally unrelated to and divorced from work activity, and makes no mention of it even at the end of the article which frequently contains the name and workplace of the writer. If you wish to include the name of your workplace, ask permission. This caution is not intended to restrain potential writers. Rather, it is intended to ensure that you are rewarded by praise and compliments from all colleagues at all levels, and to maximise mutual trust and understanding.

EXERCISES

Exercises 1—3 are designed to help you make specific plans to contribute to the nursing literature. The exercises can either be used in a personal basis or form part of a writing workshop programme.

EXERCISE 1

Write a 200-word essay, using free-flowing prose, relating to the topic 'Why I should write for publication?'. Include a brief description of areas of special experience, knowledge or interest which would form the basis of any future publication. Identify a specific time goal, six months' distant for example, during which an attempt will be made to publish one small item.

EXERCISE 2

Identify at least four journals to which written material might be submitted for publication. Briefly describe the reasons for these particular journals being chosen, and argue as to their appropriateness for this particular purpose.

EXERCISE 3

Write a 200-word letter to a real or imaginary journal, the subject of the letter being a reply to an article or letter contained within that journal. If possible, the letter should be submitted to the journal for publication. Bear in mind that journals are highly selective about the material they publish, in some instances one item may be published for every five submitted. However, you should also regard the construction and submission of such a letter, even if unsuccessful, as a valuable exercise in the development of writing skills.

Chapter 3
Resources for Writing

Part of the art of successful writing is in being able to recognise, find and utilise a number of resources which are of assistance. The beginner often, wrongly, feels that he/she must write in virtual isolation from others, only then will the writing be of *real* value and be unique. More experienced writers know that there are a number of resources, including people, who must be utilised if the best possible level of result is to be achieved.

Clearly, not all resources will be available to, or used by, an individual writer on all occasions. My purpose is to remind you that these resources are available and should be used. There is certainly no need for you to feel alone or isolated from others who can be of assistance.

PROFESSIONAL EXPERIENCE

The most important resources available to you are experience, training and knowledge. Despite the great significance and importance of these resources, professional writing being impossible without them, we frequently undervalue them. During a visit to a hospital I asked a group of nurses to describe their work to me. It was clear that a number of experienced nurses undervalued their ability to comment on the role of the nurse, making such statements as '*I've* been in nursing for thirty years, you better go and ask some of the younger nurses, they know more about it than I do'. Contrast this negative attitude toward experience with that of the medical profession for example, in which the value of experience is given full recognition.

The most important resource which nurses have is nursing experience. It is unique in that only a nurse may have it.

IDEAS AND INSPIRATION

Although some (lucky) nurses have a special aptitude for innovation, inspiration, originality and generating ideas, all have the ability to be inspired and generate new ideas. For the majority this requires some effort. However, it is possible for all nurses to develop this skill and use it as a writing resource.

Some nurses believe that they cannot write because 'they have nothing to say' or 'they don't have any new ideas'. The reality of the situation is that *all* nurses can write if they wish to, and that *all* nurses have something of importance to write about should they wish to do so.

A good starting point is to make a decision that you *will* put pen to paper, and that you do have something relevant to say. The next step is to draw from professional experience and to look to it for ideas and inspiration. For example, you may have realised whilst lifting a patient that serious difficulties were encountered in applying the theory taught in the college of nursing to the job of lifting a patient in bed. (Only a person with a nursing experience and background is in a position to make this observation.) Now that an important idea is beginning to develop it is time to put pen to paper and begin to write.

PREVIOUS WRITING SKILL

All nurses have developed a level of writing skill in a number of areas. We know that nurses in many countries will have written essay-type answers for exams, all will have written essay-type answers for coursework, and all practising nurses will be currently involved in writing clinical reports on patients. These valuable experiences can easily form the basis for further developing writing skills.

You may underestimate your ability to bridge the gap between writing for examination and other purpose, and writing a polished finished article for publication. Although there are some obvious differences between these two types of writing, the gap is not as large as might at first be thought. More importantly even the most experienced writers do not produce their 'end product' at first attempt. Providing you are willing to write and refine the writing three or four times, a polished and readable end product *will* emerge.

PUBLISHED MATERIALS

Most writers rely in some way on previously published materials. (Chapter 6 includes a discussion of how to make reference to these.) However, you can make additional use of previously published material in a number of learning ways. First you can see what a successfully written piece of material looks like, feels like and how it is presented. Published materials represent a model from which you can work. In using a published work for this purpose you are able to examine how language is used (and abused), how the material is broken up by headings and subheadings, how diagrams, graphs and tables can enliven text, and the means by which references are built into the publication.

If the material you are writing requires a summary, examination of a published article which includes a summary may be of help. If an article is being prepared for a particular journal then it would be prudent to scrutinise the articles appearing in that journal recently to get some 'feel' for the styles and format of that journal. Remember that the materials published in a particular journal represent successes from which you can learn.

PEER GROUP ASSISTANCE

You should have no hesitation about discussing ideas with colleagues. Initially, this will help to clarify thoughts about the material you propose to write. There is no doubt that having to explain ideas to another person causes us to be much more precise about what we mean. Look for, and expect, support and encouragement from your colleagues, particularly those in more senior positions. Indeed, bearing in mind the importance of literature to nursing as a developing profession, all nurses have an obligation to support, encourage and reward those of its members who are writing for publication.

Having started to write and develop a first draft you should show this material to colleagues with a knowledge of the subject. Their assistance in reviewing the material has two important functions: they can review its contents as individuals who have a thorough knowledge of the subject; they can also comment on it as prospective readers of the eventual article.

If possible, earlier and subsequent drafts of the material should be shown to a colleague who has publishing experience. If no such colleague is available in the immediate locality, there is no reason why you should not contact successful writers even though they may not know you personally. In general, those with experience in publishing are often very willing to help beginners.

LIBRARIES AND LIBRARIANS

In constructing any piece of material for publication you will wish either to 'read around' the subject informally or to undertake a formal literature review of it as part of its construction. In either event access to one or more professional libraries, and to one or more specialist librarians, is essential. At a local level such libraries might include those at the college of nursing, college of education, college of technology and the university. In general, you will have generous access to library facilities, and will find the staff in these libraries helpful and cooperative. Many local libraries participate in the interlibrary loan scheme which means that members have free access to every other library through this scheme.

Access to regional and national libraries is also available, some provide specialist bibliographies and general and specific advice, in addition to lending the usual library materials. Although the staff in many such libraries prefer to be contacted by letter, many may be contacted by telephone directly and will discuss your particular requirements.

Libraries and their staff are *extremely* important resources for the beginner writer. In particular, the assistance and advice from experienced librarians, many of whom have a thorough understanding of the nursing literature, will be most valuable. It is my experience that librarians are most willing to give assistance, particularly to the beginner who is unsure about how to make best use of a library.

PUBLISHERS

The basic sequence of events in writing for publication is: the writer writes, the publisher publishes, and the reader reads. The publisher, as intermediary between writer and reader, has a central role to play in maximising the skill of the writer. Publishers, or more usually their editors, are accessible and are most helpful in giving advice to the potential writer.

Somewhere near its Contents list page, if not on it, a journal provides its address and telephone number for enquiries about subscriptions; this section also usually contains information regarding its editor and editorial staff. The editor should be contacted as ideas are developing, any advice given or points made by the editorial staff should be considered seriously. Also, bear in mind that they are in a better position to be of assistance if the information which they receive from you is more rather than less detailed. It would be insufficient to write to an editor and say 'I am proposing to write an article about the nursing process'. However, it would be more appropriate to write identifying yourself, your post or affiliation and say 'I am proposing to write an article about the nursing process and enclose an outline of the proposed article'. This additional information will enable the editor to assess the possibilities of your work.

Advice about the general requirement and style of journals and books should be sought from the appropriate publishers or editors; this aspect is covered in greater detail in chapters 10 and 11. Remember, they are in the business of publishing and cannot do so unless writers write. They are eager to encourage and help writers, particularly beginners. Regard them as a resource to which you have full reasonable access.

TYPIST

Although all the preliminary work may be done in pencil on one side of the paper with very large margins and spaces for corrections, you should have the end-product typed. This applies to most examples of writing, with the possible exception of some types of coursework, and may be an absolute requirement of certain writing such as theses and works for publication. Unless you have the appropriate typing skills it is as well to employ a professional typist to do the job. They can usually be obtained from a local agency or, more frequently, by asking around the secretarial staff in your place of work and hiring a typist to do the job privately. There is no doubt that well-typed material and the assistance of a good typist are a very valuable resource.

VISUAL AIDS

On occasions, you may wish to reproduce material in forms other than the written word. If simple graphs, tables or charts are to be used then you might be able to do this personally. However, if other forms of artwork are necessary then the audio-visual aid department, printing department or the photographic department should be contacted for advice and assistance. Although this resource may well have to be paid for by you, such costs may not be as prohibitive as is at first thought. If it is anticipated that these services may be necessary, it is as well to go and discuss requirements with the appropriate staff.

It is obviously important that any use of illustrative materials should be discussed with the prospective publisher. It could be that the publisher is willing to provide the appropriate artwork so long as you supply a rough drawing or clearly describe what is required.

In any event you should remember that you are not confined only to the use of written words, the use of other forms of presentation should always be considered when necessary.

TEXTBOOKS

A number of textbooks are of use in relation to writing. These include a dictionary, a thesaurus and books such as this one which are designed for those who wish to develop writing skills. In addition, some publishers may refer writers to specialist textbooks which deal with indexing, writing style and use of references. A number of such texts are contained in the Recommended Reading at the end of this book. You should *never* struggle on alone in the belief that you cannot and should not employ and use the many resources which are available. All the preceding resources, and others, should be fully utilised by the beginning *and* experienced writer.

EXERCISES

Exercises 1—3 are designed to help you recognise resources which are available, and how to make use of them. The exercises can either be used on a personal basis or form part of a writing workshop programme.

EXERCISE 1

Write a 200-word letter to an editor of a journal outlining an idea which you have for an article. The letter should contain the idea and a brief outline of the shape and content of the article. As with other pieces of writing, this letter may well have to go into its third or fourth draft before you are happy with it.

EXERCISE 2

Itemise the local, regional and national resources which you are able to identify as being of assistance to a beginning writer. Include the name, address and contact person in relation to the resource. Identify local and other individuals who could be contacted by you in order to discuss your written work.

EXERCISE 3

Choose one subject about which you feel you are able to write by virtue of your knowledge and experience. Write a 500-word essay in which you illustrate the types of knowledge and experience that you have and that would be important in relation to this particular subject. Do not be hesitant about 'blowing your own trumpet' in this exercise, the purpose of which is to demonstrate why *you* in particular are eminently qualified to write about the chosen subject.

Chapter 4
Writing Style Development

The purpose of considering writing style is to maximise the quality and readability of the written work. The whole point of putting pen to paper is to convey your thoughts and ideas to the reader. Although writing style is a very individual subject, and no absolute rules exist which cover every situation, there are a few general points which may help you develop a clear writing style. The emergence of a clearly written paper will be assisted if consideration is given to the planning, structure and content of the paper prior to it being written.

PLANNING

Planning begins with the advancement of often vague ideas which will form the subject of the paper. At each subsequent stage as it progresses from vague ideas in your head to a complete paper ready for submission for publication, careful planning will make the work of producing the paper that much easier. This planning phase, which is equally relevant whether a piece of coursework, dissertation or item for publication is being produced, is a crucial part of the writing process.

There is no doubt that the longer an idea is given to mature and evolve in your mind, the easier it becomes to get that material on paper. Although you should be careful about spending too much time 'thinking it over', you must spend *some* time thinking about the subject before putting pen to paper. A colleague who is an excellent thinker and writer uses the time spent on long motor-car journeys to develop ideas, construct the outline of an article, and is ready to write a near perfect paper at first draft. Although not all of us have this kind of facility, 'thinking time' given to the preparation of the material in advance of writing it is time well spent.

During this thinking time, make rough notes, for example general headings with brief explanation, which will be used to form the skeleton of the written material. These rough notes may initially appear unimportant but they can be of much assistance when giving thought to the structure of the paper.

During this planning phase the requirements of the publisher, if the work is to be published, or the requirement of the person who will examine the work should be obtained and read very carefully. You must be clear about what is required, for example in terms of style and length, at as early a stage as possible.

STRUCTURE

The structure and shape of the written work should be explored, with appropriate notes being taken with regard to it. At least three separate, but related, items need to be considered in this part of the writing process, they are: sections, order of sections, and size, or extent, of sections.

Sections

The material must be broken up into sections of appropriate length. Examples of these sections are chapters in books, major parts of an article, and paragraphs within parts of an article. Although there are very few hard and fast rules with regard to how a piece of written work should be broken up into various parts, the subject is of considerable importance. The number of headings, subheadings, sub-subheadings and sub-sub-subheadings used will clearly depend on the length and complexity of the subject, the identification and division of points relevant to the subject but different from each other, and, when required, further subdivision introducing another related unit of thought or information.

An aid to the development of this skill is to examine previously published pieces of work, paying particular attention to how the sections are broken up. Remember, these pieces of work represent successes which have been given a great amount of scrutiny by writers and editors. When writing, you should pay particular attention to the structure of the material and make careful decisions about its sections. Finally, when written material is offered for review to your colleagues, they should be requested to comment on the various sections of the material.

Order of sections

The order and sequence of the main sections should be carefully planned in advance of writing. Most writers are fairly clear about the first and last sections of the paper, the introduction and conclusion, however the material which comes in between these two parts often causes some concern. There are two possible ways of minimising this difficulty. The first is to examine the proposed structure and look for a logical sequence of sections, each part being placed in relation to other parts because a definite decision has been made as to its placement. A second, and possibly overlapping, approach is to look for a natural sequence in the parts of the structure. A good example of such a predetermined sequence of sections is the written research report. Such a report relating to 'the role of the nurse' might contain the following parts.

Part 1 Introduction
Part 2 Literature Review
Part 3 Research Method
Part 4 Pilot Study
Part 5 Main Study
Part 6 Data Analysis
Part 7 General Discussion and Conclusions

For some works a structure may have to be developed for that particular purpose. For example, if a ward sister is preparing a description of how she developed the nursing process in her ward, that description might have the following parts:

Part 1 The Nursing Process. Definition and description
Part 2 Phases of the Nursing Process
Part 3 Historical Development of the Nursing Process
Part 4 Documentation and the Nursing Process
Part 5 Implementing the Nursing Process
Part 6 Discussions, Problems and Plans for the Future

Providing that some consideration is given to the sequence of sections, there should be few problems with this area of writing. All that is required is that you remember that every item and section appears, in relation to other items and sections, where *you* wish it to appear. Nothing should be left to chance or accident.

Size of sections

Although the size of the different parts of a piece of written work is very individualised, it should never be left to chance. A section with the same title, literature review for example, may constitute very different proportions of the total length of two different pieces of written work. In an essay which is being handed in for coursework requirements the section entitled 'Literature Review' may attract 10% of the total marks. Bearing in mind that many such essays have a maximum length, it would be inappropriate to devote 90% of the total length of the work to reviewing the literature. However, it might be more realistic to devote 10% of the total length of such an essay to that section. By contrast, an article which is designed to review the literature on a particular subject may appropriately devote 90% of its volume to the review.

As with other aspects of writing, you have to make personal decisions as to the length of particular sections. The important thing is that you realise that the length of a particular section is a question about which you must make a definite decision. As with sequence, the length of sections must not be left to chance. Rather, an estimate of the optimal length of each part should be made as soon as possible. (See page 77 for a description of how to estimate word length.)

CONTENT

The content of the paper will have been predetermined by the choice of subject matter. Only the chosen subject, and any related matter, should be discussed. It is for you to decide what should be included and what should be excluded, remembering that only those items which you particularly want to include should be contained in the work. If items are to be presented which are of peripheral importance to the subject, but nevertheless are related to it, you will wish to demonstrate this relationship.

Remember, the point of putting pen to paper is to convey ideas to the reader. This should be done in a way which is clear, to the point and as attractively written as possible. Care must be taken not to 'get off the track'. When you have completed the work, scrutinise it and ask yourself 'Do I really wish to include this?' Clear, readable material will be easier to produce if you frequently ask 'What do I really want to say?'

Many works include a mixture of fact and opinion; it is necessary to ensure that these two are not confused in the eye of the reader. Ideally, sections containing fact should be separated from sections containing your opinion. If this is not possible then steps must be taken to inform the reader of what is fact, and what is opinion. For example, this may be done by presenting facts as follows: 'the majority of nurses are female'. Opinions may be expressed as 'in my (or "our" if there is more than one author) opinion, the quality of nursing care is steadily improving'.

Writing

Having planned the material and made decisions about its structure and content, all that now remains to be done is to write the material. Writing should be started as quickly as possible, remembering that a number of further drafts will be necessary before the final stage is reached. The use of jargon, repetition, and ambiguous statements should be avoided, but these can be edited out as the draft process continues. Rough notes may be converted into a first draft, then a second draft, then a third draft, and then a final draft. Try reading each draft out loud to yourself to hear the flow of words, and ask colleagues to review the various drafts. It is extremely rare for a first or second draft to be satisfactory.

For all but the final draft, writing should be done in a manner most conducive to your own maximum achievement. The novice may find that using a pencil on one side of the paper only, leaving wide margins and large spaces between each part of the written material facilitates redrafting. The previously devised plan relating to the structure and content of the material should now be 'filled out'. The amount of words which has been allocated to each part of the work will now be used in relation to each heading, subheading and so on.

Although it may be more usual to write the parts of the paper in the same sequence as will be found in the final draft, this is not always the case nor is it always necessary. If you find it easier to write a middle or end part before writing the earlier part, feel free to do so. This is much better than spending long periods of time waiting for inspiration to 'get started' on the first part of the paper. All that needs to be done here is that the different parts of the paper are written on their own pages and subsequently rearranged in the correct order. Using this approach for a book, it is wise to number the pages with chapter and page number, for example 4.1, 4.2, 4.3 and so on.

The ability to write plain readable English, or whichever language you are using, is the hallmark of successful writing. Although this may not emerge in the first draft of a piece of work, unless you have an exceptional talent, it can be achieved in later drafts. Example 1 shows how the first draft of an essay, badly written in order to illustrate the point, can be examined and made more readable in the second draft.

The ideas expressed in example 1 are important and, with some effort on the part of the reader, readable and meaningful. However, by rewriting the essay in the form of a 'second draft' you should find it easy to improve the style. Before moving from the first to second draft, the essay should be examined for means of improvement. For example, it contains the three distinct points which have been rearranged:

1. The nursing process is increasingly used by nurses.
2. The nursing process consists of a number of phases, each of which must be documented. They are:
    Assessment
    Planning
    Implementation
    Evaluation
3. The writer has implemented the nursing process and has plans for extending its application.

Despite the valid theme of the essay, it contains a number of easily remedied faults.

Most of the sentences are overlong and occasionally repetitive, the beginning may be 'forgotten' before the end is reached. A number of distinct, although related, parts are contained within the essay; these parts include a short introductory and concluding statement.

The essay has been rewritten in example 2 to show how material may improve between a first and second draft, an improvement which can easily be achieved with minimal effort and objective criticism. The use of underlining of key words in the essay is intended to highlight the major points and sections in it. When used in a piece to be published, the underlining would indicate your preference for the key words to be set in italic type.

The development of a high quality of writing skill is something which can be achieved providing you are willing to invest some time and energy in it. The second requirement is that you are willing not only to appraise and criticise your written work but to invite and accept comments from colleagues.

Although grammar and punctuation are not the principal concern of this book, that being left to the authors of the relevant text in the Recommended Reading list, a few common concerns will be discussed. They have been selected both because they are common and because they can cause beginning writers considerable difficulty which is relatively easy to rectify.

Words should be short, sharp, meaningful and understood by readers. Each needs careful selection and placement within the sentence. If in doubt about the exact meaning, or spelling, consult a good dictionary. Where possible, use a variety of words with the same meaning, consulting the thesaurus for alternatives. Neither the thesaurus nor dictionary should be used to find a longer or 'more impressive' word.

Sentences should be neither too short nor too long. Readers must be able to grasp the meaning of the sentence without having to reread it, or first break it into its component parts.

A *paragraph* is a group of sentences (occasionally just one) in which you present one topic. If the paragraph is becoming over-long, in excess of 100 words for example, consider if the material is really only dealing with one topic.

Quotation marks are used in writing principally to designate the beginning and end of words or sentences which are being quoted directly from the work of others. There are several types, but the two most commonly used in Western literature are: single ' ' (sometimes referred to as inverted commas) and double " ". British printers adhere to the use of the former, whereas American printers employ the latter. Placement of punctuation outside or inside the closing quotation mark also varies between countries; for work not to be published your commonsense and consistent application would suffice. Quotation marks are also used to draw attention to words used in an unusual context, such as slang or colloquialisms; and more

<u>The Nursing Process A Personal Experience</u>

Given that nurses are in the best position to
make a nursing assessment of the nursing needs
of their patients, and given that all nurses
probably recognise the need to make such an
assessment prior to making decisions about
patients' nursing needs and subsequent nursing
care, the first part of the nursing process,
the part which is commonly referred to as the
assessment must be carefully carried out as
the first and very important part of
the nursing process as the quality of all subsequent nursing care will stand or fall on this.
Having made a nursing assessment, and having
first ensured that all appropriate information
relating to the patient has been carefully
collected in order to ensure that a proper
nursing assessment has been made, the next
step is to make decisions about the nursing
care which will best meet the nursing needs
which have been identified by the previously
made nursing assessment, this next phase of
the nursing process is commonly referred to
as the planning phase, planning relating to the

Example 1 Awkward first draft.

nursing care which will now be provided. Having made decisions about the nursing care plans, and documented this as will have previously been done in relation to the assessment, the nurse will now proceed with implementing the nursing care which has been planned, the implementation phase concerns the actual delivery of care which is designed to deal with the problems identified in the assessment phase as was described in the earlier part of this paragraph. Implementation is also recorded. Having implemented the nursing care, the outcome is evaluated in terms of whether or not it is satisfactory, if not, the nurse must go back to the start of the process and make a further assessment and, if necessary, repeat all the stages of the nursing process until a satisfactory conclusion has been reached. This is what is known as the nursing process, a very desirable way in which to organise nursing care, there can be no doubt that the nursing process is increasingly used and enjoyed by nurses in a number of countries. My experience with this approach to nursing care has been very positive and one which I hope to continue and extend.

The Nursing Process: A Personal Experience

Nurses in a number of countries are increasingly organising nursing care in a way which is
commonly referred to as the nursing process.
The nursing process consists of a number of
phases, each of which must be carefully documented.

Assessment is the first phase of the process
and must be undertaken by nurses, who are accepted as being in the best position to carry out
this and subsequent phases. This beginning
phase of the process must be carefully carried
out to maximise the outcome of subsequent
nursing care planning, implementation and
evaluation.

Planning nursing care follows the assessment;
this describes the nursing care which will mini-

Example 2   Second draft.

formally to indicate the component parts of a book or journal,
such as chapter or article titles.
   Italics are a useful method of emphasising a word or group of
words. They are the writer's equivalent of the speaker's raised
voice. 'We *must* win'. Underlining to indicate emphasis is used
in both handwritten and typewritten material. Printers unless
instructed otherwise will set all underlined items in italics
(underlining to be retained as in an equation is identified as a
'rule', and an encircled marginal note to that effect would clarify
your needs). Italic type is used formally to indicate book and

mise or resolve the problems identified in the initial phase.

Implementation of nursing care follows its planning, documentation continuing as with all phases.

Evaluation of nursing care is the final phase of the nursing process, the outcome of nursing care is evaluated as being satisfactory or un-satisfactory. If the evaluation is satisfactory, no further action need be taken; if unsatisfact-ory, then a reassessment of the patients' nursing needs will be made.

My experience with the nursing process has been very positive. Plans for extending the application of it are under way.

journal titles and also to identify foreign words other than those in common use in the language in which you are writing. In English, for example, words such as via and petit would not be italicised.

Listing, with letters or numbers, should only be used when it is essential that the items must be shown or displayed in a 1, 2, 3 or an A, B, C format. In general, this technique is one which can easily be overused and abused. It can intrude into your present-ation of ideas, and might in some instances be interpreted as 'writing down' to your reader.

Parentheses, or round brackets, are an integral part of the most commonly used reference systems: 'Jones (1983) suggested that. . .' is an example. Parentheses are also used to separate a distantly connected idea within a statement, where you might wish to elaborate or explain further or digress slightly from the main theme of the sentence as in a 'parenthetical remark'. The more closely connected idea would be shown between commas or dashes. As with overuse of listing, quotation marks and abbreviations, too frequent use of parentheses can be intrusive and distracting.

Brackets, or square brackets, are used to interpolate or insert your own words or correction within a direct quotation from another published work, as in 'When they [the writers] set pen to papre [sic] the printers. . .'. If permissible, it is often more kind to avoid the latter use and simply correct an obvious typographical error; perpetuating an innocent literal serves no purpose, especially to the source author. Brackets in varying shapes are also used in mathematical expressions.

Repetition of words and phrases, although impossible to eliminate completely, can be minimised by use of a thesaurus and by diligent editing and re-editing. However, repetition can, and should, be intentionally used as a means of emphasising an important point or for dramatic effect.

Abbreviations are necessary in some forms of writing, but run the risk of being abused in others. If for example you make frequent reference in your text to the Royal College of Nursing or to the American Nurses Association, each should be written in full the first time it appears followed by its abbreviated form in parentheses: (Rcn) or (ANA). Thereafter, the abbreviations may be used in place of the full title: Rcn or ANA without the parentheses.

Abbreviations such as i.e., e.g., and etc. are probably best written in full, if for no reason other than to stimulate the choice of alternatives and, more importantly, avoid their overuse. One occasion when the abbreviated form of words is always used is *et al.* which is an abbreviation for the Latin words *et alii* which means 'and others'. When referring to three or more joint authors of a reference you are using in the text, give the names of them all on the first occasion, thereafter give the name of the first author followed by *et al.* Thus, 'Clark, Fitzpatrick and Thyson' becomes 'Clark *et al.*' Although this convention is used in the text, it is *never* used in a list of references where all names *must* be presented. Note the full stop after *et al.* and the fact that it has been italicised by the printer following my underlining of it in manuscript.

Ellipses are used as a means of indicating that a word or words have been omitted from a sentence. Although this omission may interfere with the grammatical construction of the sentences, it can still be clearly understood. Thus 'Please, if I might be so bold, may I help you?' might become 'Please . . . may I help you?' The omitted words are indicated by the use of three points . . . inserted in the middle of a sentence, with a fourth point or appropriate closing punctuation if the omission occurs at the end of the sentence. In fairness to your readers you must make sure that you do not inadvertently 'select' a part of the sentence which conveys a meaning which is different from the general intention of the original writer.

Capital letters should always be used at the beginning of proper nouns, New York and James for example. Confusion sometimes arises in relation to terms such as charge nurse, general wards or departments in hospitals, or an informal reference to 'the school or the college of nursing' or operating theatre. As these are not proper nouns (they are nouns) they do not require the use of capital letters. For titles of literary works such as books, plays, journals, articles and poems each word may begin with a capital letter, alternatively each major word may be capitalised. An article title may read 'The Development of Political Awareness in Nursing' or 'The Development Of Political Awareness In Nursing'. Whichever practice is used, it should be consistent throughout the text.

Gender use, in the form of he/she and him/her may need special consideration, particularly when the terms are used often. In many nursing textbooks, authors state early in the text that nurses will be referred to as 'she', patients will be referred to as 'he'. This convention is a common one and avoids the alternative reference to nurses as he/she, and to patients as he/she. Additionally, the she (for nurses) and he (for patients) helps the reader to recognise which of the two groups is being referred to.

In some instances, particularly if you feel that reference to nurses as 'she' might be unacceptable to the reader, he/she and him/her is perfectly acceptable.

A third alternative is to write in such a way that the terms he, she, him and her are not generally used. Although this approach requires a more careful choice of words it can be done. Consider this passage which avoids the use of he/she and him/her:

> 'My spouse is a nurse, having been one for five years. With both children now student nurses, there are three nurses in my household. When I first asked a colleague to suggest why nursing was such a popular career, the reply indicated that 'working with people' might be an important factor'.

The same passage, rewritten without avoidance of gender identification would be:

> 'My wife is a nurse, having been one for five years. With my son and daughter both nurses, there are now three nurses in the household. When I first asked a colleague to suggest why nursing was such a popular career, she replied that 'working with people' might be an important factor'.

The use of a gender style requires decisions to be made. Once you have decided on a style, keep to it.

If the work is not being published, careful reading by you and a friend will minimise these potential problems. If it is being published, problems can be ironed out as the manuscript goes through its various draft and proof stages. Although publishers obviously prefer to receive a manuscript which is well-developed in terms of style, presentation and grammar, they will also be helpful and considerate if it has some rough edges. Publishers will *not* reject good ideas because the spelling or sentence structure is bad. Rather, they will encourage and help you to improve your style to maximise the presentation of your ideas.

When writing, make full use of a dictionary, thesaurus and textbook on the use of the English (or your own) language.

GENERAL GUIDELINES FOR EFFECTIVE WRITING

Effective writing is being able to convey, using a minimum of words, ideas and information to the reader in a way which is clear and readable. The following general guidelines, which are not in any order of priority, are offered as aids to the beginner.

Become familiar with the subject *before* you begin to write. Even if you are a 'specialist' in the subject, improve your level of knowledge by reading around it.

Organise your thoughts on paper, thinking carefully about the structure and sequence of the parts of the work. Do not assume that the best possible sequence will be arrived at without careful and deliberate planning.

Ensure that the material is prepared to meet the requirements of the examiner, reader or publisher. Make yourself familiar with the marking criteria, if the material is to be examined, and with the style and general requirements of the editor if the work is to be published.

Write clearly and briefly, demonstrating a good command of the language in which the paper is to be written. Remember, simply written and easily read material reflects a high level of writing skill and a thorough understanding of the subject.

Avoid overdependence on lists and abbreviations such as e.g., etc. and i.e. Lists and abbreviations can be minimised for the former by the appropriate use of sentences in the form of prose and for the latter by the use of the word or term. Skill in writing *can* be achieved with practice.

Do *not* strive for perfection in the earlier drafts of a paper, it defeats the exercise of drafts and could defeat your ultimate goal. (See Examples 1 and 2.)

Be prudent in the use of references to published materials, overuse can be as much of a problem as under use. If the work is to be published, ensure that the reference system used meets the requirements of the journal or publishing house.

Set yourself a firm timetable for completing the written work by deciding to write a specific number of words in a given time. For example, you may decide to write a 1000-word first draft of a paper over a two-week period.

Be critical of your written work and invite colleagues to review it for you, asking them to point out the 'good' as well as the 'bad' aspects.

Finally, believe that you *can* write and that you have an important contribution to make to your profession's literature.

EXERCISES

Exercises 1 and 2 are designed to give you some experience in the development of writing skills. The exercises can either be used on a personal basis or form part of a writing workshop programme.

EXERCISE 1

Write a 500-word essay on any subject, regard this as a first draft which will be 'polished' in subsequent drafts. Do not sit and wait for inspiration which will lead to prefect writing, just write!

Examine the essay and list its component parts. Rearrange these parts into a more logical sequence.

Rewrite the essay paying particular attention to the grammar and general presentation. Rearrange the parts of the essay to form a more logical and desirable sequence.

Ask a colleague who is familiar with the subject of the essay to read it and comment on style, grammar, general layout and sequence of parts.

Write the final draft of the essay.

EXERCISE 2

Read through a recent issue of a professional journal and pay particular attention to the content, structure and writing style used. Select two articles which, in your opinion, are either well or poorly written from these viewpoints.

Write a one-page critique of each of the articles demonstrating their strength and weaknesses in structure, planning and writing style. Include some suggestions as to how the problems in the poorly written article may be rectified.

Chapter 5
Illustrations

Illustrations are any type of presentation, other than straight forward prose, which is used to add to the impact of the written word. They include photographs, tables, line drawings, flow charts and other illustrative forms. Some works are incomplete without illustrations, others do not require them, and in others they might be optional or even intrusive. You must decide if words on their own are adequate, or if additional visual material is necessary. In any event, the decision to include or exclude illustrations should never be taken lightly, or left to chance, you should always ask, 'Do I need to include illustrations and, if so, which ones would best add to the quality and readability of the paper?'.

Although the writer is often able to make decisions about the use, and possible choice, of illustrations it may be worthwhile discussing this with a graphic artist or photographer. If the work is being prepared for publication, the inclusion of illustrations *must* be discussed with the publisher at a very early stage.

When preparing work, such as coursework and dissertations, which is *not* for publication, each illustration should be placed in the text close to the point at which it is first referred to. If insufficient room for it remains on the page, it should be placed on the next one. In either event, reference to the illustration in the text should read: 'Table 1 shows the distribution of marks between respondents' or 'Figure 5 demonstrates the differences between the posture of elderly men and young men'.

If the material is being prepared for publication, the publisher's instructions may ask you to incorporate the illustrations into the text as described in the preceding paragraph or, more commonly, to place them all at the end with full instructions as to where they should appear. If the illustrations are to be placed at the end, then they should each be on a separate page, should be clearly identified by number or title or both, and should have a clear indication *in the text* of where they should be placed, such as 'Place Table 1 near here'.

Because the illustrations used in this book are *examples* of, rather than actual, tables, figures and the like, I have referred to them as Example 1, Example 2 and so on.

A small sample of the more commonly used forms of illustration is discussed in this chapter, a brief examination of a selection of textbooks and journals will confirm that an almost infinite variety of techniques exists. Indeed, you may obtain ideas and inspiration by reading others' published works. The points made about each type of illustration, although typical, will vary between publishers from whom detailed requirements should be obtained.

PHOTOGRAPHS

Because photographs can be expensive to include in a work, many publishers wish them to be kept to a minimum or not used. When they are accepted, they invariably have to be black and white. The use of colour, being that much more expensive to publish, is reserved for subjects such as dermatology which require it, or for works unrestricted by a higher selling price.

High quality black-and-white photographs in the size range 152 mm × 101 mm to 254 mm × 204 mm (6″ × 4″ to 10″ × 8″) should be submitted unmounted and uncut. Any instructions, for example the figure number, should be written on a sticky label *before* it is stuck to the back of the photograph. Paper clips or staples should never be used to attach material as they may leave marks which appear when it is reproduced. If the photograph has to be cut, or cropped, to a smaller size, this should be left to the publisher, with a mark on the back in crayon to indicate the material to be used. If there could be any doubt to publisher or printer as to which is the top edge, this too should be indicated in crayon.

Photographs can often be used to describe something which is virtually impossible to capture in words, human feelings or a landscape for example, and can add an obvious 'human touch' to a paper. They should never be included unless they are felt to be necessary, and add something to the quality of the work.

Packaging used to send the photographs to the publisher should be such that no damage is done to the contents. When necessary, particularly if human subjects are included in the photography, formal written permission to publish the photograph may be necessary from the person or persons shown.

Alternatively, the publisher may be instructed to use a masking technique to hide the identity of subjects.

LINE DRAWINGS

Line drawings are often used to illustrate the type of material which would otherwise be conveyed by photographs. Although never having the quality of photographs, they have the advantage of not requiring the agreement of their human 'subjects' or their permission to publish. In some instances, a line drawing may be the best way of illustrating an idea or event. For example, they are probably the best means of demonstrating anatomical and physiological subjects such as the production of urine by the kidneys, the transfer of urine to the urinary bladder and the expulsion of urine via the urethra.

The construction of good quality line drawings is outwith the skill of all but the most artistic of writers, it is more usual to employ an artist for the purpose. Example 3 shows typical finished artwork of such a commissioned drawing which carried the instruction: 'Draw a thirty-year-old female nurse in a library looking at a book'.

Line drawings required for a book should not be commissioned until you have discussed them with the publisher or editor, who may prefer to have final artwork done by the house itself. The reasons for this range from technical to aesthetic, and all that may be needed from you are clearly labelled, rough pencil drawings.

TABLES

Tables are usually used to present numerical information in summary form, and, like text, they are read from left to right. They are probably the most widely used *and* abused form of illustration; because of their popularity, many writers wrongly assume that little thought needs to be given to producing them. As with all forms of illustration, tables require careful thought and planning. Example 4 illustrates a number of common errors which are made in constructing a table. Although it is unusual for all errors to be made in the same table, each is relatively common.

The deliberate errors in the table shown in Example 4 are:
Title   The title is not sufficiently descriptive of the contents

Example 3 Line drawing.

of the table. A more appropriate title would be 'Distribution of nursing staff by grade in Hospital X'. If there is more than one table in your work, the title should be preceded by the word *Table* followed by its appropriate number in sequence. Table numbering permits more accurate cross-reference in text and, if the work is to be published, placement of the *complete* table as near to its text reference as possible avoids breaking from one page to another.

1st Column The use of abbreviations within a table is strongly discouraged when, as is the case in this table, there is ample room for the title of each staff group to be written out in full. Also, the material in each column *must* be presented consistently.

2nd Column It is customary to indicate, where appropriate, the total number of items which will appear in a column.

Numbers of Nurses

Grade	Numbers in each grade	% in each grade
Admin. (1)	22	4.059%
R.N's	104 (3)	19.18%
Enrolled Nurses	156	28.78%
Stu.N's	80	14.760%
Pupil (2) Nurses	40	7.380%
Nursing Asst's	140	25.830%

1.   Mostly males.
2.   Mostly females
3.   This included bank nurses.

Example 4   Common errors in tables.

This should have been done as: Number Of Nursing Staff (N = 542)

3rd Column   The numbers in this and other columns must be presented consistently *and* 'in line' to minimise possible confusion. Thus, each number should be calculated to the same number of places after the decimal point. Also, the decimal point of each entry should be aligned exactly with all others in that column. Finally, there is no need to present the per cent sign   % in relation to each entry, a single per cent sign above or to the right of the first entry in the column is all that is required.

Table Note   When you wish to enliven facts with additional information but do not wish to increase the size of the table with more columns, a table note may be used. The table note references (asterisks, daggers and the like *or* letters *or* numbers) should be chosen with the table content in mind. When letters or numbers are used, their sequence should read from left to right, as the table is read, and *not* from the top to the bottom of a column.

Totals Below each column containing percentage of other values, a total of the values in the column should be presented.

Example 5 corrects the deliberate errors made in Example 4.

A common error is to overload a table to the extent of overwhelming the reader with data. It is always better to present a set of data in a number of smaller tables, rather than trying to crowd it all into one.

Table 1.   Distribution of nursing staff by grade in Hospital X.

Grade	Numbers of nursing staff (N = 542)	Percentage of total in each grade
Administrators (1)	22	4.06
Registered nurses	104 (2)	19.19
Enrolled nurses	156	28.78
Student nurses	80	14.76
Pupil Nurses (3)	40	7.38
Nursing Assistants	140	25.83
Totals	542	100.00

1.   Mostly males
2.   This includes bank nurses
3.   Mostly females

Example 5   Correction of common errors in tables.

Do not overuse tables, or any form of illustration for that matter. The failure to use appropriate means of presentation is as much of a problem as the use of many tables and figures with no more than a line or two of text in between each.

GRAPHS

As with tables, graphs are used to present numerical information in an appealing and informative format. Such information, referred to as *data* if it has been collected for research purposes, may well be presented in the form of prose. Although factual, the presentation without illustration may be difficult to understand, and fail to make the desired impact. Consider the following:

The District General Hospital has 2,482 staff, 542 of whom are nurses. Of the 542 nurses, 22 are administrators, 260 are trained staff, 140 are nursing assistants and 120 are in training. Of the 260 trained staff, 104 are registered nurses the remainder are enrolled nurses. Of the 120 nurses in training, 80 are student nurses, the remaining 40 are pupil nurses.

This simple information, although possible to understand with some effort, would be more easily assimilated if presented in tabular or graphic form. Many varieties of graphic presentation would be appropriate for this data, including the pie chart or bar graph.

PIE CHART

The pie chart is most often used to show proportional distributions such as the percentage distribution of trained and untrained staff in a given work force. The tools required to construct a pie chart are: a pair of compasses or some other means of drawing a perfect circle, and a protractor for dividing the circle into its predetermined parts.

In constructing the pie chart the size of each of its sections are calculated as: *each 1% = 3.6°*. Thus 22 (4%) of the nursing staff are administrators, therefore $3.6° \times 4$ of the chart (14°) relates to that grade. With 260 (48%) of the nursing staff being trained nurses, $3.6° \times 48$ of the chart (173°) relates to that grade. There are 140 (26%) nursing assistants, therefore $3.6° \times$

26 (94°) relates to that grade; and 120 (22%) are in training, therefore 3.6° × 22 (79°) relates to that group. This information is presented in the form of a pie chart in Example 6.

The pie chart is used only when there is a smaller, rather than larger, number of items to be included. If many items are included, for example in excess of ten, the large number of relatively small parts will be difficult to distinguish from each other. Similarly, as parts become smaller and represent tiny percentages, 1% for example, it becomes very difficult to indicate to the reader what such parts represent.

The contents of the pie chart can be entered either within the pie chart, as in Example 6, or outside the pie chart with a line from the item to the appropriate part of the chart. Alternatively, a colour or some other form of coding such as lines or dots can be used within the chart, and an appropriate key placed immediately below or within the caption.

Distribution of nursing staff in Hospital X

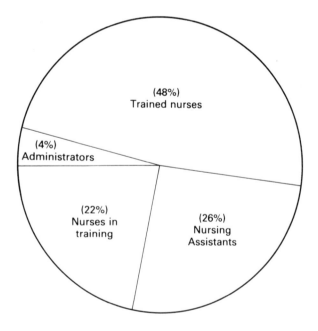

Example 6   Pie chart.

BAR GRAPH

The bar graph also presents numerical data in pictorial form, it can be either horizontal or vertical. Example 7 is a vertical bar graph containing the same data presented in Examples 4—6.

The individual bars in the graph each represent one part of the data, they are drawn to scale and are separate from each other. Each part of the graph must be carefully labelled. The factor related to by each bar, 'trained staff' for example, must be placed in *or* near the bar.

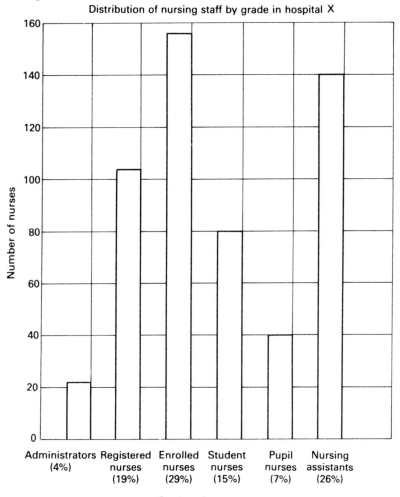

Distribution of nursing staff by grade in hospital X

Grades of nurses

Example 7 Bar graph.

The axis relating to measurement, the vertical axis in this instance must be carefully drawn to scale. Although the scale in this example starts from zero, this need not always be so. For instance, if the graph is designed to show the difference between the numbers of staff in each grade and the smallest number in any one grade is 550, the vertical axis may well begin at 500 rather than zero.

SOCIOGRAMS

Sociograms are useful means of describing the frequency with which individuals interact with each other. Such a description does not require an illustration if a small number of participants are involved in the interaction, two for example. However, the difficulties of an unillustrated description of interaction frequency among ten or more participants are easy to imagine.

In constructing a sociogram, decisions need to be made regarding the individuals to whom it will relate, and to the information which it will contain. In Example 8 the interactions between a charge nurse and his staff have been recorded, solid lines representing those interactions initiated by the charge nurse, those with hatched lines representing patient-initiated interactions.

When the numbers of people to be included in a sociometric illustration are large, it might be best to produce several sociograms rather than to place all the information into a single presentation. There is no hard and fast rule regarding the acceptable complexity of a sociogram, trial and error should precede the final decision.

The sociogram is a highly specialised form of presentation which allows easy identification of individuals who rarely or never interact, *isolates*, and those who frequently interact, *stars*.

ORGANISATIONAL CHART

The organisational chart presents the relationship between individuals, or positions, in various parts of an organisation. This is a further example of using a technique to present information which would be difficult to explain or understand in essay form. Example 9 is one way in which an organisational chart may be used.

Simplicity of presentation is an essential feature of the

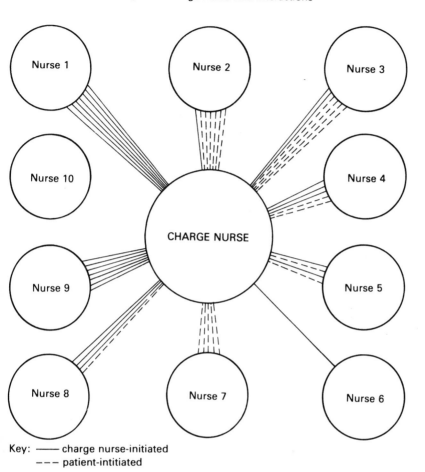

Analysis of charge nurse staff interactions

Nurse 1   Nurse 2   Nurse 3

Nurse 10   Nurse 4

CHARGE NURSE

Nurse 9   Nurse 5

Nurse 8   Nurse 7   Nurse 6

Key: —— charge nurse-initiated
     – – – patient-intitiated

Example 8 Sociogram.

organisational chart, material which is too complex for a single chart should be placed in two or more.

FLOW CHART

The form of illustration particularly useful when presentation of the parts and sequential direction of an idea or concept is being made, is the flow chart. For example, although a description of the phases of the nursing process using only words is quite possible, the additional use of a flow chart will

Typical nursing management structure in hospital

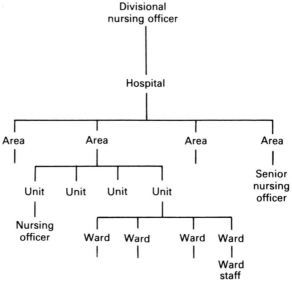

Example 9 Organisational chart.

considerably enliven the description. Example 10 illustrates
the visual impact of a flow chart.

Experimentation with various types of flow chart helps to
establish which presentation best describes a particular idea.
As with all forms of illustration, innovation and experimentation are necessary to achieve best results.

USE OF ILLUSTRATIONS

When deciding whether illustrations are necessary and, if so,
which ones to use, consider the following points to optimise
their impact. These apply equally to article, book or other forms
of writing such as coursework, exams, and research reports.

You must obtain and study any constraints imposed by
examiners, publishers, degree-awarding bodies and the like. If
the instructions do not refer to the use of illustrations or do not
answer your specific questions, then the appropriate individual
must be contacted regarding this point. It can be disheartening
to find that time or money has been wasted on illustrations only
to discover that they cannot be included in the submitted work.

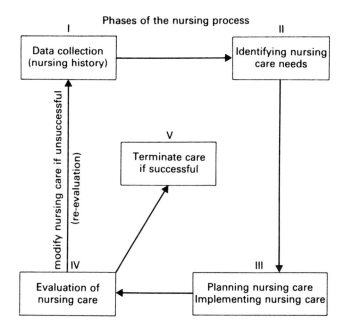

Example 10 Flow chart.

If illustrations can be used, you must ask yourself whether they should be used. Including them 'because everybody else seems to' is as much a mistake as not using them when they would be appropriate. Clearly, this question cannot be properly answered unless you are fully aware of the purpose, advantages and variety of differing types of illustration. If the material can be presented in the form of well-written prose, then illustrations may detract from the work. When words alone are inadequate for the purpose, or where illustrations will add to the visual impact of the presentation, then drawings, photographs, tables and the like should be used.

The purpose of the illustration will determine the type which is used. For example, the physical features associated with the ageing process may be best conveyed with a photograph or a good line drawing. Alternatively, a table may best describe numerical information. If the most appropriate type of illustration is unclear, or is possible by using more than one approach, then experimentation with a number of types and discussion with colleagues or the publisher may make the choice easier.

If illustrations are used, they should be as 'independent' of the text as possible in that they should, with a well-chosen title, require minimal *explanation* in the text. The amount of discussion which an illustration requires in the text should be carefully considered and *never* left to chance. If tables are used to summarise numerical information, you must decide how much, or how little, of the tabular information should be repeated in the text or as an appendix.

All illustrations used should be as simple as possible, long and complex tables or graphs defeat the whole purpose of their use. Readers dislike complex and over-full illustrations, ideally they should be short, sharp, to-the-point and should have an accurate descriptive title.

The number of illustrations used should be 'in balance' with the total length of the text, too many being as much of a problem as too few. Although there is no hard and fast rule about their proportion in relation to text, they are probably too numerous if exceeding more than one third of the total text extent. As discussed at the beginning of the chapter, they should appear as close as possible to their reference in text or on separate sheets at the back for a publisher. Readers should *never* have to search through a text to find illustrations.

Each illustration should be appropriately identified and numbered, Figure 1 or Table 5 for example, and should be used in the text as well as above or with the actual illustration. Reference to it in the text should *not* read 'in the following table'; 'Table 5 *below*'; or 'See Table 5 which is presented *below*'. The reader should simply be requested 'See Table 5' or informed that 'Table 5 summarises the findings . . .'.

Finally, you should assume that mistakes can be made in the use of illustrations, these can be made by you, the typist or publisher. As with the text in general, all illustrations must be carefully checked and rechecked.

EXERCISES

Exercises 1—3 are designed to give some practice in the choice and use of illustrations. They can either be used on a personal basis or form part of a writing workshop programme.

EXERCISE 1

Write a 300-word essay which contains the opportunity to illustrate material by using three or more different illustrative techniques. Do not use illustrations at this stage.

EXERCISE 2

Consider which of the available illustrations will best suit the needs of your essay, experiment with different forms of illustrations.

EXERCISE 3

Rewrite the essay and include the chosen illustrations. Where illustrations are to be photographs or line drawings, prepare the instructions to be given to the photographer or artist.

Chapter 6
References

Whether or not your writing is to be published, you may wish to make formal references to other published materials, a possible exception may be when you are writing under some examination conditions. Two terms need to be looked at closely here, *reference* and *published*. The term *reference* relates to the bibliographical description author, title and other features of a published work. The inclusion of a formal reference to a work has only one purpose, to direct the reader to it. For example, if you make formal reference to a published work by Jones (1960) the reader must be given enough information to enable him/her to find that publication with minimal difficulty.

Published is the second term which needs examination. In this chapter the term is used to describe any idea or information which is made available to others by means of either the written word, which may be a formally published work or a privately distributed piece of material, or something 'published' verbally such as at a conference. The term can also refer to forthcoming publications such as those which have been accepted for publication by a journal. If the material being referred to has not been formally published, an unpublished paper or conference presentation for example, the 'author' of the work *must* be contacted personally and written approval to refer to the work obtained. An exact copy of the material which is to be referred to should be sent to the original author for approval; this way the author is given an opportunity to check that your interpretation is correct. This constraint does not, of course, apply to the mention of formally published materials such as articles, books and other publications. If, however, you are using extensive portions of that material, or are using another writer's illustrations, you *must* seek written permission from that author and/or the publisher or whomever holds the copyright for the work. If in doubt, ask for permission.

Example 11 incorporates the various details which you would include if you were seeking permission to reproduce a lengthy block of text, illustrations or tables from a copyright holder.

Permissions Editor
Blackwell Scientific
Publications Ltd
Osney Mead
Oxford OX2 0EL

1 Cottage Close
Kearnsly
Lancs LC1 3BX
4 July 1984

Dear Sir/Madam:

In my forthcoming book, Writing in the Health
Professions, to be published by Campbell &
Holbrook Ltd in 1985, I would like to use the
following material from Sarson et al. (1983)
The Nurse Journalist, published by you:
Page 178, paragraphs 1-3, from line 2 beginning
'The nurse involved in writing articles...' to
line 36 ending '... and adheres to the prin-
ter's schedule'.
Page 84, Table 5.3. Ratio of Nurse Authors
to Other Health Professionals in the United
Kingdom, 1964-1984.
Page 179, Figure 9.1. The Application of
Proofreading Symbols.

I would be grateful if you would grant me
permission to use the material specified above.
Appropriate acknowledgement will, of course,
be made.

Thank you for your help.

Yours sincerely

Ann Tides, RGN, RHV, PhD
....

Permission is hereby granted to Dr A. Tides,
RGN, RHV, to use the above-specified material from
Sarson et al. (1983) The Nurse Journalist, Oxford,
Blackwell Scientific Publications Ltd in her
forthcoming book, Writing in the Health Professions,
to be published by Campbell & Holbrook Ltd in 1985.
World rights (included/not included)

....
Permissions Editor, Blackwell
Scientific Publications Ltd

....
Date

Example 11 Permission letter.

References are used for constructing reference lists, bibliographies, annotated bibliographies and reading lists. Although each of these uses is similar in that it makes use of references, each has an important difference.

REFERENCE LIST

When writing for coursework, an article or a book, you will usually refer to extant works, and place these references either in a list at the back of the book or article, or at the end of each chapter. While this is the general rule, there are exceptions and not every piece of such work will include references. Although the basic function of the inclusion of references is to direct the reader to the materials referred to, the reasons for their initial inclusion must be examined. The major reasons for including reference materials are to learn and to inform.

To learn about a subject

Irrespective of the topic being written about, you quickly realise that your knowledge of the subject may be much more limited than you at first anticipated. Therefore, it is prudent to learn about the subject by reading what others have written about it before committing yourself to paper. This approach is neither new nor unusual in that most writers and students will look for ideas, knowledge and inspiration from the written works of others. It is not, of course, being suggested that you simply repeat the material which you have read. Old ideas and existing knowledge added to personal ideas and knowledge, however, can result in a better contribution to the literature. In short, there is no point in 're-inventing the wheel', the job of the writer is to be aware of existing knowledge and *add* to it.

To inform others of the relevant literature

In the course of reading around a subject prior to writing about it, you will invariably encounter a large amount of published material about which you will wish to inform your reader.

When a paper by Jones (1982), for example, is being read, you will be doing so for at least two purposes: first, to discover what Jones (1982) has to say on the subject; second, to become aware of the wider literature which has been read and referred to by Jones (1982).

To learn about research methods

The last major reason for using reference materials in your writing is of particular relevance when your paper has a research base. In this case you will have read and referred to reference materials which have helped you to learn about research methods.

In undertaking any piece of research it is vital that you take full account of the published materials about the subject in general, and of the research methods used which relate to that subject. By doing so you are able to use or adapt previously created research methods, and learn from the 'mistakes' which were made (and usually discussed) by other researchers.

SYSTEMS OF CITATION

The two most commonly used methods for incorporating references into scientific work are Harvard and numerical.

Harvard system

The most widely used, and perhaps easiest method, is referred to as the *Harvard* system. It involves giving the surname of the author in the text, followed by the year of publication. Usually, both are enclosed in parentheses unless the author's name is part of the sentence. Such a reference might read:

> 'The use of the nursing process is regarded as being essential to the delivery of high quality nursing care (Jones 1982). This view was supported in a subsequent paper by Smith (1983).'

When using the Harvard system remember that, apart from the ideas and information expressed by the writer you are citing, only the surname of the author and year of publication are included. At the end of the article or piece of coursework you will include a list containing full bibliographical details of all the references cited in the text. The title of the list will be the single word *References*, beneath which will be an alphabetically arranged list of the references. Although the presentation of

book references will be slightly different from that of journal
references, there are a number of similarities (see Example 12).

The numerical system

In a numerical system, publications cited (referred to) in the
text are numbered as they appear, in sequence. At each point in
text where information from another source is cited, its number

The relationship between the ratio of trained

nurses to untrained nurses and the quality of

care given to hospitalised patients is commented

on by a number of writers (Black 1981, White 1982

and Green & Blue 1980). In a paper by Scarlett

et al. (1979) this relationship is described as

being:

'positive in the sense that the greater the ratio

of trained staff to untrained staff, the better

the quality of care' (p.4, my italics).

A rather more constrained view is expressed

by Brown (1983) who suggests that an increase

in the ratio of trained to untrained staff may

(my italics) result in improved care. Mustard

(1983), who suggested that far too little was

known about this subject, recommends that it

urgently required researching. A similar view

is expressed, although it was not acted on,

by Blue (1980).

Example 12 Harvard reference system.

is inserted in parentheses or as a superscript. The text might appear as:

1 'In a more recent paper (14) it was shown that . . .' *or*
2 'In a more recent paper[14] it was shown that . . .'

If different parts of a published piece are referred to in text, and you have used the first style, the appropriate page numbers may be added to the text in addition to the number of the

References

Black, P.(1981) Staff Ratios, 4th ed. Glasgow, Thompson.

Blue, F.ed. (1980) Calculating Establishments. London, Smith-Brown Ltd.

Brown, G. (1983) Quality of care. Nursing Issues in Perspective 5, 65-8.

Green, P. & Blue, F. (1980) Staffing issues. In Smith, P. (ed.) Care and Care Measurement. Aberdeen, Clark and Thompson.

Mustard, F. (1983) Nursing Care, Vol. 2. York, Brown and Clark.

Scarlett, P., Blue, F., White, C. & Black, P. (1979) The art of caring. Nursing Issues in Perspective 1,4-8.

White, F. (1982) Trained Staff - Untrained Staff Ratios. Doctor of Philosophy Thesis, University of Scotland.

reference. For instance, 'In a more recent paper (14 p. 18) it was shown that . . .'.

At the end of the text with this system, the references appear under the heading 'References' but are listed in numerical sequence instead of alphabetically (see Example 13).

Book references

A reference to a book contains the surname and given name or its initial of the author (or editor), the year of publication in parentheses, the title of the book (which when underlined by you indicates italics), the edition of the book which is being referred to if more than one edition has been published, the city of publication and the name of the publisher. The following example illustrates an acceptable form for presenting a book reference.

Jones, T. (1983) *The Meaning of Nursing*. London, Smith.

Please note that the title of the book (underlined in manuscript has been set in italics by the printer) shows initial capitalisation of the first word and of all major words which follow.

Journal references

A reference to a journal article also contains the author's name, the year of publication, the title of the article, name of the journal (underlined) in which the article appeared, the volume number of the journal, and the first and last page numbers of the article. The example below shows how a reference to an article can be presented. The article title, unlike the italicised book or journal title, is set in roman type and uses a capital letter only for the first word and any proper names following.

Smith, S. (1983) The nursing process in Great Britain. *Nursing Perspectives in Focus* 1, 60–5.

Unpublished reference (Unpublished paper or conference presentation)

A reference to an unpublished paper, included *only* with the written permission of its author, should also enable the reader to locate the original publication directly or through its author. A reference to an unpublished (written) paper may be:

The frequency with which the nursing process
is cited in the nursing literature is increasing
(1). According to some authorities this increase
has probably reached a peak and will decline
rapidly in the next decade (2, 3 p.4). It is
also suggested that this decline in references
to the nursing process is because the concept
· is no longer novel (3 p.9).

In relation to the future development of
nursing as a profession, one research-based
study (4) concludes that the principles of the
nursing process are far more important than
the words used to label its different parts (5).

References

1. Hart, F. (1980) The nursing process.
   Nursing in the 1980s 10, 11-12.

2. Alisk, R. (1983) Nursing Care. Manchester,
   John.

3. Frank, T., Jack, F. & Arkle P. (1980)
   Evaluation of nursing. Nursing in the 1980s
   10, 4-9.

4. Clark, P. & Simpson, R. (1982) Nursing
   process and development. Issues in Nursing
   Care, 2nd ed. Birmingham, Brown.

5. Ian, R. (1981) in Clark, P. (ed.) Nursing.
   New York, Black and White.

Example 13 Numerical reference system.

Franks, S. (1981) The Application of Basic Psychological Principles to Health Care Issues. Unpublished paper. Regional Psychology Unit, District General Hospital, London.

A reference to an unpublished paper which had been read at a conference might be:

Reilly, V. (1982) A Healthy Elderly Population: An Aim of Total Health Care. Unpublished paper. Opening address at National Health Care Conference, 18 July 1982. Association of Nurses, London.

GENERAL GUIDELINES IN USING REFERENCES

Ensure that the method of using and writing references meets the requirements of the person who will examine or publish the written work. If these requirements are not given to you, then the onus is on you to make enquiries about them.

Use a formal and an acceptable method of citation, such as the Harvard system or the numerical system, for presentation of references. Be consistent in the use of references and employ one system throughout. Remember that there are two common means available for citing reference material within the text. Direct quotations may be shown as:

> 'The development of nursing in the past few decades has been considerable' (Jones 1983, p. 2).

If a direct quote is used, as in the preceding example, it is usual to give the page number from which the quote was taken. The second method is to paraphrase the material which is being referred to. This method means that you use your own words to describe the idea or information which was contained in the text being referred to. For example:

> From the 1960s onwards, (Jones 1983, p. 2) indicates a substantial step forward in nursing as a profession.

With experience, you will develop the ability to vary the means by which you use reference materials in the text. Clearly it would be boring if you introduce every reference by saying 'According to'. Varying this form of introduction is personal, you will develop other forms of introduction with which you are comfortable. Other devices include the use of 'It is suggested by . . .'. 'An alternative view has been expressed by . . .', and 'Jones (1983) is of the opinion that . . .'.

The overuse of reference material is as much a writing fault as is its underuse. Indeed, it is too common for published works to be so laden with reference materials as to intrude upon the clarity of an idea and to make reading the item tediously difficult.

As a general rule references are required only when the idea, statement or knowledge being used can clearly be identified with some other writer. For example, if you state that senile dementia is age-related, there would be no need to refer to any previously published work, as this assertion is widely accepted. If, however, you are describing what it feels like to be the recipient of a heart transplant you would almost certainly wish to make reference to the published views or knowledge of some other person.

When collecting references, whether for a project or for publication, it is useful to keep some information about them on small cards which themselves can be stored in an alphabetical index system (usually under the first letter of the author's surname). The card should contain the formal reference to the piece of material, the library or some other place where the material can be obtained, and brief details of the contents of the reference material.

BIBLIOGRAPHY

A bibliography is a list of references relating to a specific subject. For example a bibliography may relate to 'the nursing process' or to 'pain' or to 'men in nursing'. A bibliography may be constructed by an individual who is interested in or researching a specific subject, who is writing about that subject, or who is studying the subject. The list of references of which the bibliography is composed is presented in alphabetical order. A number of libraries provide bibliographies on a number of subject areas on request. For example, if you are researching or writing about 'cross-infection in coronary care units' it may be worthwhile asking your (local and national) libraries if they have a bibliography on the subject.

A common error which is made in relation to bibliographies

and references is to confuse a bibliography with a reference list. It will be remembered that a reference list is a list of references which are cited in, or referred to, in a text, and which appear in a list at the end of the text under the heading 'References' or 'Reference list'. Such a piece of written work may or may not have a bibliography in addition to the reference list. Whilst all items in the reference list will have been referred to in the text, none of the items in the bibliography will have been referred to in the text. Thus, items in the bibliography relate to the subject of the text, but are in addition to those references used in the text and subsequently contained in the reference list.

Title   Community Psychiatric Nursing

Clark, V. (1978) Psychiatric nursing. Community Psychiatric Nurse 18, 6-8.

This paper, written by a community psychiatric nurse contains an excellent account of the role of the community psychiatric nurse (CPN). A detailed description of one CPN'S work on a day-to-day basis is given. Although the writer makes no reference to other publications on the subject, an excellent bibliography is included.

Jones, P. & Smith, O. (1981) The Work and Function of the Community Psychiatric Nurse. East Grinstead, Clark and Faston.

This book is the first comprehensive text on the subject and, although limited to the work

Example 14   Annotated bibliography.

Annotated bibliography

A bibliography is a collection of references relating to a specific topic, pain or community psychiatric nursing for example. An *annotated* bibliography is one in which each of the references is accompanied by critical or explanatory notes. Producing an annotated bibliography is a particularly useful exercise in relation to students' coursework. A student may be requested to write an essay on a given subject, make appropriate references to other published work *and* produce an annotated bibliography of a given length (see Example 14).

of the CPN in one part of England, has an

application to the United Kingdom generally.

The writers have chosen to emphasise the practi-

cal aspects of the subject, but do take full

account of the underlying theory. References and

reading lists accompany each chapter, and exam-

ine the subject from a multidisciplinary viewpoint.

Letterpoint, P. and Peert, W. (1981) <u>Psychiatric</u>

<u>Nursing in the Community</u>. Atlanta, Ga., Free-

way Press.

The North American origins of this book have,

unfortunately, resulted in an examination

of the subject from a relatively narrow, paro-

chial viewpoint. This criticism is made in the

light of the author's claim in the Preface that

the text would discuss psychiatric nursing in

the community from an international perspective.

READING LISTS

A reading list, which will come at the end of a written piece, contains a selected number of references which the writer feels would be useful for the reader. As with the references contained in the bibliography, the references contained in the reading list have not been cited or referred to in the text.

It is rather unusual to find a reference list, *and* a bibliography, *and* a reading list at the end of a piece of written work. If references are used, then obviously a reference list must be included at the end of the article, chapter or book. A reference list *may* be followed by either a bibliography or a reading list. The ability to use references is a very important part of the development of writing skills, the inability to refer formally to the published work of others being severely limiting. Although the majority of beginning writers have little experience in using references in a formal way, the skill can be developed easily by all who are motivated to improve their writing skills. My experience has been that many students can develop this technique successfully after a sixty-minute class, whilst others 'get the hang of it' within a few days of being introduced to the topic.

EXERCISES

Exercises 1—4 are designed to facilitate the development of your skills in relation to using references, they can either be used on a personal basis or form part of a writing workshop programme.

EXERCISE 1

Write a 200-word essay and incorporate six references using the Harvard system. Three of the references should be to journal materials, and three should be to books (one by an author, one by an editor and one by either). Two of the references cited in the text should be presented as direct quotations and at least two should be paraphrased.

At the end of the essay, the reference list should be formally presented as described earlier in this chapter.

EXERCISE 2

Write a 200-word essay and incorporate six references using a numerical system. Three of the references should be to journal materials, and three should be to books (one by an author, one by an editor and one by either). Two of the references cited in the text should be presented as direct quotations and at least two should be paraphrased.

At the end of the essay, the reference list should be formally presented as described earlier in this chapter.

EXERCISE 3

Construct a bibliography, with the references listed alphabetically by author surname, relating to a subject of your choice. The bibliography should contain at least ten works and should relate to a subject in which you are currently interested. Three of the entries should relate to materials which have not been formally published.

EXERCISE 4

Construct an annotated bibliography of a subject of your choice. A minimum of five references should be included with each annotation being between 50 and 150 words long.

Chapter 7
Coursework and Examinations

Although different, coursework and exams are similar in that they are both submitted in order to pass some form of academic test. Whilst both may possibly be submitted for subsequent publication, their prime purpose is to enable you to obtain a registration, diploma or degree. Despite the discussion of each of the items being presented separately, there is considerable overlap which should be taken account of when reading each section. Also, the requirements of individual institutions, and teachers within them, will vary. This chapter is offered as a general guideline which will enable you to ask the right kind of questions before putting pen to paper. It is essential that the individual requirements of the institution and/or teacher be obtained and examined closely before writing begins.

EXAMINATIONS

My discussion of exams is confined to essay-type exams which offer greater scope for the use of writing skill. It will be assumed that you will take appropriate steps to establish the format of the exam and will know whether essay-type or objective-type questions are to be used. This discussion is also directed to the kind of exam in which there is a choice of questions, and where examples of past examination papers are available.

Past papers

Assuming that no significant change in the general format and content of the examination subject has taken place, it is advisable to study exam papers which have been set during the past five-year period. This will enable you to 'get the feel of' past papers and to increase familiarity with the way in which exam questions are set. Although, in most instances, teaching staff will ensure that students sit past papers under exam conditions as part of class tests, you should supplement this experience by 'sitting' past papers in your own time.

Most teachers are willing to mark and/or discuss answers to

past papers which have been written by students as part of private study. The amount of feedback, no matter how brief, which is made available by teaching staff is valuable.

Exam structure

In most instances teaching staff will provide information about the structure of the forthcoming exam in terms of the number of questions, any sections into which the paper is divided, and the general area to be covered by each of the sections. If possible, it is useful to establish whether there is to be a compulsory distribution of questions in the paper. For example, examinees might have to answer five questions during the three-hour paper, including at least one question from Section A, one question from Section B and one question from Section C.

Exam preparation

Students have a clear responsibility to study, practice and know the subject of the exam well. Any reservations or confusion about the subject matter should be identified as early as possible and discussed with the appropriate teacher prior to the exam. It is essential to realise that a thorough knowledge and experience of the subject matter does *not* guarantee that you will be able to formulate a satisfactory answer under examination conditions. Although a thorough knowledge of the subject matter is a necessary requirement for success in the examination, it is also necessary that you have considerable practice in answering exam questions, under examination conditions, prior to the actual exam.

Initially, examination practice may be undertaken with the assistance of books or course notes, or allowing some additional time. As more skill develops then the course notes or books are no longer used, and the time allocated for the questions becomes identical to that available in the exam. Whenever possible, this type of practice work should be shown to and discussed with an appropriate teacher.

The exam

Enter the exam room with a watch and all other required materials. Read *every* word of the exam paper carefully, this includes introductory material, instructions and the exam questions themselves. Reread every item on the exam paper. Make decisions about which questions are to be answered, and in which order. If the questions can be answered in any order, it may be best to start with the question about which you feel most confident.

As with other forms of writing, it is necessary to give some thought to the structure of the answer before giving further thought to finer detail. It is usually permissible to do 'rough work' within the answer book, and in most instances this rough work must be deleted by having lines drawn through it prior to the end of the exam. Planning for the structure of the answer may well be done in the form of rough work.

Ensure that you leave yourself some time at the end of the exam for checking and rechecking all written material. Although major changes cannot be made during this time, minor changes which may add to the quality of the answer can often be made.

General hints for examinations

Read the question paper very carefully paying particular attention to the distribution of marks within the parts of the question.

Spend some time preparing an outline structure for the answer.

Answer the question which was asked. This means reading the question carefully.

Confine your answer to the question in hand.

Avoid 'waffling' and getting off the point.

Admit to being uncertain as to the answer of a small part of a question. For example if you feel attracted to a particular question but are unable to remember a particular drug dose which is asked for, feel free to answer the question and admit that you have forgotten the drug dose. However, you must tell the examiner how you will find out what the correct drug dose is.

Write clearly and legibly. Although examiners will take account of the fact that the material has been written under examination conditions, the manner in which the answers are written and presented will influence them. No credit can be given for items which cannot be understood.

Use headings and subheadings to break up the answer. This makes for easier reading and gives the answer a clearer structure and more professional finish.

Use references in the answer, although you will probably not be expected to remember full details of the reference or to produce a perfect reference list.

Use drawings, graphs, figures or tables in the answer. These may be desirable in some instances, essential in others.

Use all of the time which is available for the exam. There can rarely be any excuse for leaving before the end, any extra time should be used for checking the answers.

As with all types of writing, answering examination questions requires not only a thorough understanding of the subject matter but also investment of time in terms of obtaining practice at writing. Many students feel that self-imposed examination practice is unnecessary because the specific content of the exam can never be predicted. However, the purpose of exam practice is not to predict the content of the exam, it is to get practice at writing under examination conditions, and to revise the subject matter of the exam. With this kind of practice you not only will enter the examination room with more confidence but will be able to concentrate on *content* and less on structure.

COURSEWORK

Coursework is forming a more integral part of several types of study. In many courses students have a constant, on-going and fairly heavy coursework load. Whilst reading the following discussion of coursework, you should bear in mind that individual institutions and teachers will have their own requirements. The contents of this general discussion are offered as an addition to the specific requirements of your institution or teacher.

The coursework question

The subject of the coursework should be read very carefully and understood. If you have any doubts whatsoever about the meaning of the question or if your understanding seems to differ from that of other students, it is essential that you go to the appropriate teacher at once. Some coursework 'questions' are set as statements which the student is asked to discuss. For example,

'Making a nursing assessment is an early and important part of the nursing process. Discuss this statement'.

The key words in this statement are 'nursing assessment' and 'the nursing process'. These parts of the statement should feature prominently in the answer.

Marking criteria

Teachers usually, although not always, indicate the marking criteria. In that case the parts of the coursework may be broken down and individual marks allocated to each part, or marks may be allocated for things such as references, general presentation and grammar. Any such instructions should be retained and referred to throughout preparation. They are a useful guide to preparing the structure, and to making decisions about where to place the emphasis. If the teacher is awarding 10% of the total marks to conclusion and discussion, it is reasonable to assume that approximately 10% of the total length of the work may relate to that subject. Similarly, if a proportion of the marks are to be allocated for the appropriate use of references, it is essential that reference material be included.

Structure

Thought must be given to the general structure of the answer. A series of headings and subheadings must be prepared, these will constitute the framework of the answer. Although these may well be modified and changed as the answer progresses, it is best to start off with a framework in mind and on paper. An estimate of how much time, in terms of words, will be allocated to each part of the answer should be made at this point.

In the question concerning the importance of nursing assessment as part of the nursing process, an initial structure might be:

Discussion of the nursing process
Extended discussion of assessment
The need for a *nursing* assessment

Alternative types of nursing assessment
Description of a nursing assessment framework preferred by the writer
How to make a nursing assessment
Nursing assessment in relation to other parts of the nursing process
Conclusion and general discussion
Reference list

Writing the coursework

It is probably best to construct a shortened version of the coursework prior to its completion. Although reference to class notes and appropriate textbooks will be necessary, the teacher will be looking for the inclusion of new material from you.

When writing materials of a specific length, as is the case with coursework, estimate accurately how many words per page you write. This is best achieved by taking a few samples of pieces which you have written, and estimating the number of words you write on, for example, a page. This can be done by counting the number of words which you have written on a typical 10-line piece of work, dividing the number of words by 10 and multiplying that number by the number of lines on the page of paper which you use. If you find that, on a typical page, you write 300 words then it is not difficult to make an estimation of how many words will be on a half- or quarter-page. Although this method of estimating is commonly used, you may wish to 'play safe' and count every word in the work, particularly if you wish to confirm your methods of estimation.

The coursework, which should be clearly and pleasantly written, should be 'packaged' in an attractive manner before submission. The first page should be a title page containing certain points of information, for example:

Smithfield College of Nursing
Year III (Student Nurse Course)
Miss J. Smith
Class: Social Skills in Nursing
Teacher: Mr F. Jones
Title: 'Nurse-Patient Communication'
Estimated Length: 2,500 words
Submission date: 2 March 1985

Page two should be a contents page clearly indicating the parts of the coursework, such as:

Submission

Hand in the work on or before the final submission date. To prevent loss of work, it is best to submit the material using the agreed procedure. Trusting the delivery of work to unreliable mailing systems or by leaving it outside the teacher's door will be inviting disaster. Do make sure that it is delivered safely and personally and, if possible, retain a copy.

The following hints relating to coursework are offered; they should be read in conjunction with the materials relating to exams, dissertations and theses.

General hints for coursework

Prepare a piece of coursework which is of the requested length. Although many teachers may well allow a leeway of 10% above or below the prescribed length, others may deduct marks.

Use a formal and recognised reference system. If the teacher indicates no preference for a particular reference system, then one should be chosen and used throughout.

Give careful thought to the structure of the coursework answer, and to the entire piece as a package. Plan out the title, contents and other pages carefully.

Answer all parts of the question. Marks will not be given to material which, although of considerable interest, does not constitute an answer to the question.

Include figures, graphs, tables and other material as appropriate.

Feel free to discuss the proposed answer, in general terms, with the teacher. This is particularly important if you have any concerns regarding interpreting the question.

Ask the teacher about marking criteria, if this has not been given to you. If marking criteria are made available it is essential that particular attention is paid to them.

Set aside time in which to do the coursework, do it earlier rather than later.

Make sure the material is clearly written and well-presented, typewritten if possible.

Ensure that the work is submitted on time, and reaches the appropriate teacher safely.

On return of the coursework, feel free to discuss the marks allocated with the teacher, particularly if you are unsure about where you 'went wrong' or where your work was particularly successful.

Because coursework is prepared without the pressures of examination-room conditions, teachers are looking for a high quality of work. This high quality, in terms of structure, presentation and content, is certainly possible if you are willing to invest some time and energy in preparation. Coursework preparation is also a valuable opportunity for learning about the subject, and for its revision prior to formal examinations.

EXERCISES

Exercises 1 and 2 are designed to increase awareness of giving adequate thought to planning the structure and presentation of essay-type examination answers and to coursework planning. They can either be used on a personal basis or form part of a writing workshop programme.

EXERCISE 1

Select an essay question of the type which you will have to answer in a forthcoming examination.

Construct an outline answer, using headings and subheadings, and indicate the approximate length of each part of the answer.

Discuss the outline answer with an appropriate teacher/lecturer.

EXERCISE 2

Select a topic which may form the subject of a piece of coursework for a course of study.

Prepare a structure for the coursework answer, then 'fill out' the headings and subheadings by adding two or three sentences to each part. Complete the coursework essay to meet the (invented or real) coursework requirements of the teacher.

Finally, discuss the work with an appropriate teacher/lecturer and ask him/her to mark it.

Chapter 8
Dissertations and Theses

The differences, in required writing skills, between dissertations and theses are sufficiently small as to make a combined discussion of them appropriate. All the points made in this discussion apply equally to dissertations and theses, although some dissertations will be more limited in their depth and scope than will be some theses. In the interest of brevity, only the word *dissertation* will be used, however the word should be interpreted as meaning dissertations *and* theses.

Dissertations in the United Kingdom are often used as a requirement for courses other than those leading to a higher degree. For example, students on a diploma course at a college of higher education or those undertaking some master of science courses may have to produce a dissertation. The work may take the form of a research proposal, of a complete research project, or some other form. In most instances you will be informed of the marking criteria to be used, and will prepare your work under the close supervision of an appropriate member of staff. Although many of the points which were made earlier in relation to coursework are of relevance to dissertations, the latter are usually much more detailed and formal in their structure and presentation. Detailed requirements of the structure and presentation of the dissertation must be obtained and followed.

So far as is possible all materials written in connection with the dissertation should be made in duplicate, with the 'extra' copy being kept separate from the original. This is to safeguard against the rare, although possible, loss of the only copy of the work. As is the case with any written material, including that submitted to a publisher, you should consider using registered or recorded delivery if it is to be mailed.

STRUCTURE

The structure and subsequent appearance of a dissertation are of particular importance. Although structural requirements vary between institutions, and possibly between teachers, Example 15 is a typical one. You must, nevertheless, make absolutely sure that you adhere to the specific requirements laid down by the institution for which the work is being prepared.

The dissertation consists basically of three major parts: those items which precede the actual dissertation, the dissertation material, and finally, those items which follow it. It is traditional to number the pages of the items which come before the dissertation in Roman numerals. The pages of the dissertation, starting with the first page of the first chapter, are numbered in Arabic numerals. Items which come after the dissertation are also numbered in Arabic numerals, and are numbered consecutively with the dissertation itself. A typical structure might be as follows: the first typewritten page inside the binding will be the title page. Although details on arrangement may vary Example 15 is common.

The next page after the title page will be a 'Contents page', it

```
Professional Relationships in Health Care



Jean Smith M.A., R.G.N.



Submitted in partial fulfilment of the require-

ments for the degree of (title of degree or

diploma) of the (name of institution awarding

the degree or diploma)



Title of degree or diploma



Name of institution


Year of submission
```

Example 15 Title page for dissertation or thesis.

being an exact reflection of the structure of the dissertation and containing every major item in it. Example 16 is one type of dissertation structure.

Once you have described the contents, and therefore the structure, of the work, each item in the contents list follows in the sequence you have shown.

Item   Page Number

Contents page   i

(The following items are listed on the

contents page and appear after it)

List of tables   ii

List of figures   iii

List of appendices   iv

Acknowledgements   v

Summary   vi

Chapter 1 (Title)   1

Chapter 2 (Title)   14

Chapter 3 (Title)   25

Chapter 4 (Title)   38

Chapter 5 (Title)   45

Appendix 1 (Title)   51

Appendix 2 (Title)   52

Appendix 3 (Title)   53

Reference list   54

Bibliography   56

Example 16 **Sample dissertation structure.**

List of tables

The list of tables will include the number, full title, and the page on which it appears. The order of the listed tables should be as they appear in the text, table 1 appearing first, table 2 second and so on.

List of figures

The list of figures is similar to the list of tables, with the figures within the text being referred to by number, title and page number.

List of appendices

The number (or letter), title and page number of each appendix, which will appear at the end of the dissertation, will be listed here.

Acknowledgements

The help of those individuals, groups or institutions which have made completion of the dissertation possible should be mentioned here. In this section you thank those people who have facilitated the completion of the work.

Summary

The inclusion of a summary of the entire work, written to a specific length, is a frequent requirement. On occasions the word *Abstract* is used rather than *Summary*, depending on the institution.

Each of the preceding five items should begin on a new page, should be well presented in terms of structure, and should be given maximum visual appeal by the use of good layout and typing skill.

Chapters

The chapters or major sections of the dissertation now appear. Each should begin on a new page, be given a number such as 'Chapter 1', and should be given an appropriately descriptive title.

Appendices

Each appendix should also begin on a new page, be given a number or letter such as 'Appendix 1' or 'Appendix A', and should be given a title.

Reference list

All references cited in the text should now be listed under the title 'Reference List'. The form in which the references are presented will depend on the reference system used in the text, the Harvard system or numerical system for example.

Bibliography

A bibliography containing those references consulted by you, but not cited in the text, should be included.

BINDING

Dissertations have usually to be bound to meet the very specific requirements of the institution concerned. Facilities for binding may be available within the institution or may have to be arranged through a commercial binder. In either event it is essential that the precise requirements, in terms of size, colour, style and form of binding, are made known to those undertaking the binding.

INSTRUCTIONS TO TYPIST

In all but a very few instances, dissertations should be transferred into typescript before submission. The reasons for this requirement include:

First, you will wish to ensure that the reader can understand the material. Although some handwriting is relatively easy to read, it is often either difficult or tiring to read for a period of time.

Second, if dissertations are to be made available for public use, through interlibrary loans for example, they must be presented in professionally prepared typescript.

Third, there can be no doubt that a reader will be positively biased in favour of material which is attractively typed and professionally presented. This is also of particular importance when submitting material for publication, the physical appearance of the paper being (almost) as important as its contents. Whilst it is not being suggested that a good visual presentation is a substitute for poor content, busy readers, examiners and editors do prefer to read material which has optimum visual appeal.

Finally, the typewriter is much more accurate, versatile and consistent than the human hand, producing a much better quality of work. If possible, the technology of the typewriter or, increasingly, the word processor should be used in full for the final draft.

This discussion contains selected specifications which should be made available to a typist. It is not exhaustive, a good typist will almost certainly raise further specific points which require clarification.

Other specifications

If the material is being written to the specification of an examiner, or university degree-awarding body, the requirements must be made known to the typist. If such specifications are not available, or are felt to be inadequate, then you must design a personal list of requirements which might include the following points.

NUMBER OF COPIES

It is usual to make a copy/copies for the person to whom it is to be submitted *and* one further copy for the author. When multiple copies are required, perhaps more than two, it may be possible to use the original which has been made by the typist to produce photocopies. Although some institutions, or individuals, may not accept photocopies, it should be remembered that contemporary copying machines can make copies which are every bit as good as the original.

DATE OF COMPLETION

A realistic date, with some additional time for emergencies, should be agreed for completion of the work. If the work is longer than article length, a thesis or book for example, completion dates for each of its parts may be agreed.

A typist will need adequate time to work on a manuscript, particularly if he/she is doing the work in addition to a full time job; ensure that this is available and that a mutually acceptable date is agreed.

PAPER SIZE AND TYPING STYLE

Typing paper comes in a variety of shapes and sizes, although A4 (210 mm × 297 mm) is the most commonly used paper size in the United Kingdom t! ere are other sizes, some of which are more popular in other countries. If you are not providing the typist with paper, make quite sure that clear instructions about paper size are given.

Style relates to a number of items such as the type of spacing to be used, margin size, numbering of pages and reference system to be used. Spacing may be single, $1\frac{1}{2}$, double, $2\frac{1}{2}$ and 3, the lower the spacing number, single spacing for example, the greater will be the number of lines of typescript on the page.

Margin size instructions may range from 'the usual margin sizes' to an exact margin requirement in relation to all four margins. For example the margins of a dissertation may have to be:

Lower margin	:	40 mm
Upper margin	:	20 mm
Left margin	:	20 mm
Right margin	:	10 mm

Page numbering may relate to the exact position of the number, in the centre of the lower margin 10 mm from the lower edge for example, or to the use of Roman numerals in the earlier parts of the work, and the use of Arabic numbers in the main text. In some instances the typist may be instructed to number pages in pencil, and to refrain from typing in the numbers until the final draft stage is reached. Thus, if material has to be removed or added, it will not be necessary to change all page numbers.

The reference system should be carefully explained in order that the typist can 'keep a check' on its use by the writer.

ITALICISING AND UNDERLINING

Handwritten work may contain some sections which are underlined, but italics will not normally be used. Although all typewriters will have an underlining facility, many models are unable to italicise. Clear instructions need to be given in these respects. For example; 'items underlined in blue/black ink should remain underlined, items underlined with red ink should be italicised.' Bear in mind that publishers' printers italicise items which are underlined, unless otherwise instructed.

INSERTING EXTRA PAGES

If additional pages are inserted into a completed manuscript, the pages of the original text should not be changed if they have already been typed in. Rather, the additional pages should be added with letters after the page number. Thus, two pages inserted after page 9 would become 9a and 9b.

HEADINGS

Even the most modest of typewriters will cope with at least three orders of headings, these should be typed without underlining or ending with full stops. As headings appear in the script you should indicate their style in the margin by placing an encircled 1 to the left of the largest heading, 2 to left of the next largest, and 3 to the left of the smallest heading. These might appear in the typed manuscript as:

   ① LARGEST SIZE OF HEADING (All capitals)
   ② Middle Size of Heading (First letter of each main word capitalised)
   ③ Smallest size of heading (First letter of heading and all proper nouns capitalised)

ABBREVIATIONS

Avoid over-reliance on abbreviations. Once an abbreviation has been defined and introduced in the text, National Health Service (NHS) for example, it can be used freely subsequently. Those which should be avoided are etc., i.e., viz. and e.g. as they are easily overused with little attempt made to find alternatives.

QUOTATION MARKS

Quotation marks are used mostly to identify passages which have been quoted from other people's work; alternatively, the passage may be indented and quotation marks omitted. Single quotation marks may also be placed round words which are used in an unusual context or which are coined for a specific purpose (see also p. 33).

CHECKING THE TYPESCRIPT

Although the typist has a responsibility for checking the work, you have the final responsibility for ensuring that it is typed as requested.

A good typist not only will ensure that the work is typed as requested, but will add to its quality by examining it for errors. Make the typist feel free to offer suggestions as to how the work may be improved in terms of grammar and structure. A good working relationship with a skilled typist is an invaluable asset to any writer.

SUPERVISION

All aspects of writing, including the planning phase, should be fully discussed with your dissertation supervisor. It is standard practice to submit handwritten work, particularly in its earlier drafts, to your supervisor who will examine it thoroughly and make appropriate comment. All aspects of structure, presentation, design and content should be discussed.

EXERCISES

Exercises 1 and 2 are designed to increase awareness of the importance of *structure* to written work generally, theses and dissertations in particular. They can be used either on a personal basis or as part of a writing workshop programme.

EXERCISE 1

Select a published, or unpublished, thesis or dissertation and examine its contents in order to determine its *structure*. Compare the contents page with the actual structure, are there any differences?

EXERCISE 2

Select a published, or unpublished, thesis or dissertation and critically examine the sequence and length of its parts.

Chapter 9
Research Reports

A major feature of virtually all successful pieces of research will be the preparation of a written report. This requirement exists whether or not the research is to be published. Although writing a report is only one part of the research process, it is a particularly important and difficult part. The purpose of this chapter is not to discuss the research process, only that part of it relating to 'writing up' the work.

The preparation of a report will be necessary irrespective of the purpose for which the research was undertaken, the same principles apply to an informal small-scale study, to a doctor of philosophy thesis, and to a large-scale research project undertaken by a team of researchers.

It is often said that research undertaken by nurses and other professionals is rarely read, and less frequently implemented. This criticism may, in no small part, be that the resultant reports are poorly written. It might be argued that unless research reports are written in a form which is meaningful and readable, their potential effectiveness is drastically reduced.

Many researchers experience some difficulty in preparing a written description of their work. This discussion is intended to minimise these difficulties and should be used *in addition* to any instructions offered by the institution which has commissioned the research, or with the requirements of the institution awarding the research degree. If the report is to be published, it must be written to comply with the requirements of the publisher.

STRUCTURE

The writing-up phase of the research process should run in parallel with all other phases of the process, although it is widely accepted that an additional specific time should be set aside for this purpose. A useful starting point is to consider the structure of the report (a topic which was given some attention in the preceding chapter). Researchers, particularly the inexperienced, should remember that a suitable structure already exists in relation to the research process.

Introduction

A general introduction to the subject of the report should include a discussion of its importance and the need for it to be researched. The research problem will be clearly identified, as will the thinking process which resulted in its selection. The relationship of the work to past, current or future projects should be made clear. The background and experience of the researcher should be included here in order to place the work into a personal context. After reading the introduction the reader should be quite clear about the nature and purpose of the research.

Aims of research

A detailed discussion of the aims of the research, including the operational definition (exact definition) of the main terms used, is then presented. The aims of the work should be listed in an abbreviated form either before or after the discussion.

Literature review

A detailed presentation, review and analysis of previously published relevant literature should follow. You demonstrate how the research has been influenced by, and will develop from, existing literature. The purpose of the review is to inform the reader of relevant literature and of how it relates to the present study. Literature which is supportive to, *and* disagrees with, your research should be included.

This part of the research report will be much more easily prepared if all references previously collected are recorded on alphabetically filed reference cards. It is *absolutely essential* that a well-organised record is kept of all reference materials.

Research method

A comprehensive and detailed description of the research method will follow. It describes, in detail, *every* step of the means by which data will be collected. This description will enable your reader to understand the research design, judge its suitability and repeat it if necessary.

The population and sample selection is described, as will any sampling techniques used. If experimental methods are used, they must be reported in considerable detail. The validity and reliability of all data-collecting instruments is discussed, as will any problems anticipated.

Ethical considerations

The length of the section on ethical considerations will depend on whether or not ethical problems are anticipated. If no such problems exist, or if they are minimal, the section will be short. If ethical problems are anticipated they should be fully discussed, with steps taken to minimise these being described in detail.

Assurances regarding confidentiality and anonymity are a common feature of many research projects. The means by which these are promised to potential or actual respondents should be described, as should methods used to keep this promise.

Entry to research site

Most research studies are dependent on obtaining permission from individuals, committees or institutional managers to enter a site for the purpose of collecting data. Details of how this was achieved, including correspondence with research and ethical committees, should be covered.

Data collection

Sometimes data collection is referred to as 'The research method in action', this section describes how research data were actually obtained. Any difficulties experienced during this phase, particularly if they are likely to affect the study, should be acknowledged and discussed.

If this phase constitutes a pilot study, its outcome in terms of adequacy or otherwise should be included, as should any resultant changes in the research method.

Data analysis

Collected data are now formally analysed, described and presented in a clear and unambiguous form. Any statistical analyses used should be appropriate and meaningful to the reader.

Conclusions and discussion

The major aim of the closing section is to draw conclusions from the study while bearing in mind the limitations which it will undoubtedly have. The conclusions can be factual, based on the data, or represent your opinion. The inclusion of informed opinion is not only permissible, it is essential providing that the reader can distinguish it from fact.

The discussion will enable you to speculate about the meaning of the findings, recognise the limitations of the study and make suggestions for further research in the subject area. No new material should be introduced in this section.

Finally, a brief summary of the major findings of the study should be presented.

The items which precede and those which come after the main structure of the research report will be similar, if not identical, to those described in Chapter 8.

In addition to the structure, other aspects of the report should be considered before and during the actual research, and whilst the report is being written. The report should not develop haphazardly, during its construction these two points should be borne in mind:

Reason (Why is the report being prepared?)

and

Readership and language (Who will be reading the report and which language level will they best understand?)

REASON FOR A RESEARCH REPORT

Irrespective of how many, or few, people have an interest in the findings of a piece of research, it is necessary to prepare a written report of it. Apart from providing a permanent record of the work, the actual act of 'writing up' the work adds much to your understanding of it and helps avoid the use of generalities which are a feature of many verbal descriptions. A written report is a useful *aide mémoire* which will enable you to keep in touch with the research as it progresses.

Many reports are written up as a condition of the institution which commissioned them; preparing it may also be a condition set by a grant awarding body for example. Similarly, if the research is being undertaken in part fulfilment of a higher degree, producing a thesis will be compulsory.

In terms of a more general readership, the report has two major purposes: to make the findings available and to give details of the research methods used.

To make findings available

When you present full details of the findings of the research, you must include those which supported any hypotheses or expectations, those which contradicted them, and those which were inconclusive. When possible raw data, or liberal samples of them, should be included in addition to the more frequently used summaries of data.

A full discussion of the meaning and interpretation of the research findings will include an important 'personal' input in which you rely on personal experience and knowledge of the subject matter. In this concluding section the data will be interpreted, used to increase knowledge of the subject, and used to give direction to further research.

Important as the findings are, they are neither more nor less necessary than a full description of the research methods used.

Research methods used

In some instances only part of a report may be published, an article might contain only a summary of the findings for example. However, the full report *must* contain a detailed description of the research methods used in a given study. The reasons for including this section are in order that the reader can personally evaluate the quality of the findings, avoid similar mistakes, and use similar or identical methods.

JUDGE THE QUALITY OF THE FINDINGS

The validity and reliability of any piece of research are only as good as the methods used to obtain them. It is important that readers be given the opportunity to make a critical appraisal of the methods by being able to study them in the report. In those instances where a part of the research is published and does not include a methods section, the reader must be referred to the complete report in order that he/she can, if he/she wishes, read it and judge the quality of the methods used.

AVOID SIMILAR MISTAKES

One important reason for undertaking a literature review as part of every research study is to learn from the problems experienced and mistakes made by other researchers. The methods section should therefore discuss all problems, solutions, shortcomings and strengths relating to the methods used by you.

USE IDENTICAL OR SIMILAR METHODS

Another reason for reviewing the literature is to identify previously used methods which can be used, or adapted, in your own project. Unless these are included in considerable detail in research reports, the reader will be unable to judge whether the methods used by you are relevant to his/her research.

READERSHIP AND LANGUAGE OF A RESEARCH REPORT

Constantly bear in mind the needs of those who will read your report, and use 'language' which will be understood by them. Although the formal language of the report may be English for example, decisions will have to be made regarding the use of technical terms, mathematical language and illustrative material such as photographs, tables and figures.

Readership of the report

The report may be written in different ways depending on its readership, remembering that a reader with a background in research, for example, will have needs which are different from those of a member of the public with no such experience. Although report writers must identify their own audience, there will be individuals or groups, or both, with other requirements.

THE GENERAL PUBLIC

Readers such as the general public may have neither the professional or research background nor skills to enable them to understand anything other than a jargon-free and relatively non-technical report. A report of this type may say very little about the reviewed literature or research design, with emphasis being placed on presenting, interpreting and discussing the findings. It might be presumed that this readership has a limited understanding of research, technical or professional language.

AN EXAMINER

If the report, a dissertation or thesis for example, is being submitted for examination it must comply with the marking and examination criteria of the institution concerned. Such a work may focus on the theoretical and philosophical aspects of the research process, in addition to the more practical issues.

Dissertations and theses deliberately deal with a number of issues which are not part of that particular study, but an understanding of these being indicative of an understanding of the research process generally. For example you may discuss a range of *potential* ethical issues and their possible solution, although these were not actually experienced. By doing so you are able to indicate an understanding of an important research issue although it did not arise. The language of the report should take account of the background and research experience of the examiners. When possible this should be established in advance of writing.

A COMMISSIONING INSTITUTION

If the work has been commissioned by an institution, it may have to circulate to a large number of readers for comment or information. In this instance, you may have to prepare a summarised version of the entire work, a reduction from 50,000 words to 2,000 words would not be uncommon. If such a summary is required, this should be made known to you in advance as should the exact specifications, including its length. A limited knowledge of research language and a general understanding of the subject of the study may be assumed.

OTHER RESEARCHERS

Other researchers will be particularly interested in the research methods used, indeed an article extracted from the whole report may deal only with the research design. Similarly, full details of the statistical methods used would be included in a report prepared for other researchers. A knowledge of research, technical and statistical language may be assumed of this readership.

SPECIALISTS IN THE SUBJECT OF THE RESEARCH

Specialists, such as other nurses with similar professional backgrounds, may require a report in which the application of the findings to professional practice are fully discussed. A knowledge of professional language, the *subject* of the study, may be assumed of this readership.

Language of the report

The language of a report is, to a large extent, dependent on its readership and will include the use of 'words' 'mathematical' and 'pictorial' elements. It is unlikely that the language of a report will be exclusively of one kind, a combination of two of three types being more common.

WORD LANGUAGE

Words should be carefully chosen and written in a clear and understandable way, reports which are badly written are difficult to read and are frequently not implemented for this reason. Readers are entitled, indeed encouraged, to be suspect of a work which is difficult to read. They are justified in assuming that an ambiguous, unclear and otherwise badly written report may reflect muddled thinking on the part of its writer. It is sad that an otherwise good piece of research has less impact than it deserves because it is poorly written.

MATHEMATICAL LANGUAGE

Although not all research will make use of the numbers and other symbols of mathematical language, they form an important, perhaps crucial, part of many such studies. They may be used in tables, figures, in the text or to describe statistical concepts or findings. The range and complexity of use may vary from the simple, 'five per cent of the sample was female', to the complex, one of many statistical tests for example.

A large proportion of most professional groups, mathematicians and statisticians are obvious exceptions, will have some difficulty with mathematical language. If it is to be used for any purpose other than the most simple, percentages and averages for example, you must decide whether some explanation is required. Such a decision will obviously depend on the readership, researchers requiring much less explanation than professionals with no research background.

PICTORIAL LANGUAGE (ILLUSTRATIONS)

It is a truism that a picture can paint a thousand words, this is of considerable importance when writing a research report. The types of picture which may be used include tables, graphs, figures, line drawings, sociograms, photographs and blueprints. These are sufficiently significant to the subject of writing generally, and research-report writing in particular, to justify a chapter being devoted to the subject (see Chapter 5).

GENERAL HINTS FOR WRITING RESEARCH REPORTS

My hints are directed in particular to those who are writing a report for the first time. The list is not exhaustive, the hallmark of good report writing is innovation, imagination and experimentation with a variety of approaches. The points made are in addition to those raised in the earlier parts of the text.

Time

A common error made by beginners is to underestimate the time required to write a report. In general it is prudent to allocate one third of the time available for the entire project to writing the report. This writing time will not, of course, all be used at the end of the total available time. Perhaps one half of the writing-up time, one sixth of the total research time, will be used as the work is proceeding, the other half being used at the end of the project.

Starting to write

Writing up should start as soon as possible, when ideas about the work are first beginning to develop. Written work should be produced, however sketchy and disorganised it is, at every stage of the research. These notes will form an important part of the final report.

Remember, ideas are rarely fully developed and clarified until they are placed on paper. While it is easy to be vague and ambiguous in terms of your thinking, these faults will be more easily identified and resolved when they are placed on paper.

Write down the reasons for being interested in this particular research topic, why it is felt necessary and include as much background information as possible.

References

All references consulted in relation to the study must be recorded in an alphabetical storage system, the card should contain full bibliographical material, a summary of its contents, and a note of where it can be found. If the reference has been examined and found to be of no value to the study, this fact should be noted on the filed reference card. *This important aspect of carrying out a research study must be initiated as soon as the decision has been taken to start the work*, it is essential to the successful completion of a written report. (See Chapter 6 for a full discussion of this subject.)

Documents

All documents relating to the study, those collected as data and those used to collect data, should be carefully stored for further use. Many of these will be presented in the body of the report or as appendices. If there is any doubt as to whether a document should be included, it is as well to err on the side of inclusion.

Structure

Draft a provisional structure of the final report during the stage at which the research is being planned. So far as is possible this draft structure should contain as much detail as can be anticipated, headings, subheadings, and titles of figures, tables, line drawings and appendices for example.

The draft will, of course, be modified and remodified as the research and subsequent report writing progress. This revision will take minimal effort and will add considerably to the ease with which the report is written.

Shape

The grouping of material into chapters and sections of chapters, and the sequence of these parts is sometimes referred to as shape. The shape of major parts such as chapters will be determined by the structure of the work. The shape, in terms of the arrangement of materials within chapters, also requires careful planning. The actual size of each part of the work, and its size as a proportion of the work as a whole should be deliberate rather than left to chance. This decision will be influenced by the purpose of the report, and by its proposed readership.

Title

A tentative title for the work should be decided on at the beginning of the project to provide both a focus for the work *and* a 'label' by which it can be discussed with others. The title which should be reexamined as the work progresses and changed, if required, when the report writing is complete, must be an accurate reflection of the subject of the research. Gimmicky titles are best avoided as they will fail to indicate the contents of the report to potential readers. An example of an appropriate title might be:

'A study of the role of men in nursing'.

Detail

Good research and good research reports greatly depend on attention to detail. The contents of the report must be exact, specific, unambiguous and sufficiently detailed as to leave the reader in no doubt about its meaning. Many professionals, including nurses, regard the detail required of a research report to be pedantic and unnecessary. However, the development of this skill constitutes an important part of what is known as 'research-mindedness'.

Accuracy

As in all forms of writing, a research report demands a high level of accuracy in presenting factual material which has emerged from the research. Although this accuracy is an important feature of the presentation of numerical data, it is by no means confined to that application. Whether qualitative or quantitative data are being described in the report, you need to check and recheck what has been written. This refers to the data, research findings, and to the means used to describe them. It is particularly unfortunate if an otherwise excellent piece of research is regarded as 'suspect' because of inattention to accuracy when the work is written up.

Drafts

Allow for making up to four drafts of a research report, this will be expensive in time *and* finance if a typist is used, and should be taken into account when budgeting. In earlier drafts allow for making changes and additions, this will be made easier if wide margins are left and if pencil is used on one side of the paper only.

Earlier drafts should be shown to, and discussed with, colleagues or those for whom the work is being prepared. If the research is being formally supervised, as it almost certainly will be, all drafts *must* be read and commented on by supervisors.

The final report *must* be attractively written, easy to read, and professionally presented. Remember that, with minimal effort and relatively little expense, a research report of poor quality in terms of appearance can be transformed into a visually attractive item. Again, I do not wish to suggest that high quality presentation can ever be a substitute for high quality content. However, readers expect and deserve reports which are carefully prepared in order to make them visually appealing and readable.

Summary, or abstract

Whether or not a short summary, or abstract, is requested by those for whom the report is being prepared, it is as well to prepare one. Summaries, or abstracts, the words are being used as synonyms, may typically be of 200, 300, 400 or 500 words in length. They require considerable skill to write and should accurately summarise the *entire* contents of the work.

Confidentiality and anonymity

Unless those institutions and individuals taking part in the project, by providing data for example, have agreed to be identified, readers of the report should be unable to identify them. The writer should maintain confidentiality and anonymity by stating generally such as:

'A 400-bed district general hospital'

or

'A sample of nurses in a rural location'

or

'A staff nurse said. . . .'

or

'A consultant physician reported that. . . .'

PUBLISHING RESEARCH REPORTS

Research reports may be published in the form of the written word or by some other form such as talks at conferences or study days. The report should certainly be made available to those who commissioned the research, and possibly, either in complete or entire form, to those who participated in it. Unless there is any restriction on its circulation, every attempt should be made to make it available to as wide an appropriate readership as possible. This is probably most effectively achieved by publishing either a series of articles or by converting the report into 'book form' for publication.

In summary, the preparation of a research report requires a number of steps in addition to those required for other types of professional writing. Although the writer has the advantage of having to work to a pre-existing 'blueprint' in the form of the structure of the research process, the accuracy, detail and objectivity required in a research report call for careful attention, as is the case in all good writing.

EXERCISES

As with other types of writing skill, research-report writing can be satisfactorily undertaken providing that basic ground rules are followed. The exercises described are designed to facilitate the development of this skill. Exercises 1 and 2 can either be used on a personal basis or form part of a writing-workshop programme.

EXERCISE 1

Choose either an 'imaginary' research subject, one which you are about to embark on, or one which you would like to undertake and then:

1　Prepare a draft structure in which each of the major parts or chapters are identified.

2　Expand the draft structure to include subheadings and sub-subheadings.

3　Attach a single sentence summary to each of the parts of the expanded draft structure.

EXERCISE 2

Select a research report with which you are familiar and which contains *no* summary or abstract. *Or* use the expanded draft structure in item 3 of Exercise 1 to:

1　Construct a 500-word summary of the research report. Then:

2　Reduce the summary to 200 words.

Chapter 10
Articles

Articles form a key part of the professional literature, offering ideal opportunities for the beginner, those who have a short-sharp message to convey, and those who want to say something of relatively immediate significance. The very existence of so many nursing journals, and of those related to nursing, testifies to the importance of the article as a means of professional communication.

An unfortunate mystique surrounds the publication of articles, it is something which 'they' do and something which is practically impossible for the 'ordinary' nurse to do. The fact is that publishing in the form of articles is the business of *every* professional nurse, and that 'they' do not wish to have a monopoly on such an activity.

Journal editors are constantly on the lookout for new ideas and fresh materials, contrary to popular belief they are more than willing to consider and accept manuscripts from those who are trying to publish for the first time. Most articles, providing reasonable attention to preparation has been taken, will be published if you persevere with your efforts. Bear in mind that there are many journals to which nurses have access, including those in all countries which speak your native language. Indeed, nurses who speak a second language or who have access to an interpreter should certainly consider publishing in languages other than their own.

In identifying a subject about which to write choose the one which you know best. Remember, these are topics about which *you* have a unique experience and knowledge and are, therefore, eminently qualified to write. As nurses, we often perceive our work as being so 'routine', 'basic' and 'ordinary' that others could not possibly be interested in reading an account of it. The reality is that every aspect of nursing care has the potential for being the subject of a journal article, it simply requires sufficient imagination and innovation to identify features of it which should be described. It is not being suggested that any description of any activity or idea should be prepared for publication, particularly if it has been done many times before.

Rather, I suggest that the subject of the publication is sometimes less important than the ability of the writer to look at it in a new way, increase knowledge of it, develop new relationships between well-known facts, and challenge existing beliefs regarding well-established routines or procedures.

The major steps in having an article published are planning, writing and publishing. These will be dealt with in turn, as will each of their substeps. The detail of the discussion which follows is not intended to intimidate you, and it will not (I hope) result in the task seeming to be too formidable. The purpose of the presentation is to guide the beginner through what can be a complex task. However, with interest and motivation you *will* succeed.

PLANNING

Planning begins with a commitment to writing for publication generally, and to writing an article in particular. At this stage you need to decide whether to work on the article on your own or to invite a colleague, who may or may not have had publishing experience, to co-author the paper. This decision, a matter of personal preference, has advantages and disadvantages however you choose.

Co-authorship

A contribution from one or more co-authors should be considered only if it is known that the article requires this type of authorship and that others are willing and able to play a *full* part in its construction. Some papers, even some relatively short ones, have as many as seven authors. This number is usually hard to justify, some may have been included in the authorship because they happen to be in charge of the unit, a senior member of the medical staff, or because they 'expect' to be included. A basic rule is that a minimum number of authors be included, and that those who are should be making a significant contribution to the paper. Whether co-authors are junior or senior colleagues, non-nursing colleagues, or are experienced or inexperienced writers will vary according to the needs of the paper and of the senior author.

If more than one author is to be involved, decisions need to be made about division of responsibilities and of any expenditure and income. Who is to be the 'senior author', that is, have the name listed first in the authorship of the work, needs to be decided. It is *not* the case that the names of the authors must or should be listed in alphabetical order. In general, the first author named is regarded as the senior author of the work. In the unlikely event of a multiple-authored paper genuinely having no senior author, it may be as well to list the names alphabetically or, preferably, to draw them out of a hat to determine their sequence. Irrespective of how the listing of names is decided, the one whose name appears first will, rightly or wrongly, be given senior status. It is probably best to recognise that the individual who initiates the article idea, contacts potential co-authors, produces the first written material, provides momentum for the work, and who puts the final product together be given senior author status and be named first in the list of authors.

The idea

With a little effort you will be able to identify a number of ideas which could usefully form the basis of an article. However, the motivation to publish must be equalled by a conviction that the information needs to be shared with professional colleagues. Specific reasons for writing are many and include informing, educating, speculating, questioning, identifying issues and influencing opinion. These reasons were outlined in Chapter 2 and need no further discussion here.

As the subject of the article begins to emerge, you should ask the following questions to determine its suitability. If the answer to each of these questions is Yes, then the chances of successfully producing and publishing an article are very good.

Am I sufficiently interested in the subject? Although writing for publication is a rewarding experience, it can be difficult. Unless there is a keen interest in, and commitment to, the subject of the writing, the level of motivation will not be high enough to sustain through the difficult periods.

Do I have the necessary experience, knowledge and understanding of the subject? The subject of the article must be one with which you are familiar. In most instances writers choose a subject which has formed a significant part of the work experience. In the unlikely event of being attracted to a subject which, although of considerable interest, is outside your immediate experience, you must take time to research the subject and become sufficiently versed in it. Although it may be possible to convince an editor that one has a greater knowledge of a subject than is actually the case, this deficiency will be spotted quickly by those who read the article, if not by the editor.

Is the subject of the article novel, newsworthy, or presented in a new way? Although there is some merit in publishing old ideas, and reinforcing established practice, editors are more interested in original ideas, those which advance nursing knowledge, and ideas which are generally novel to the readership. Remember, that to answer this particular question the writer must know the subject, and have researched it thoroughly.

Is the information accurate and factual? Any information which is presented as fact must be thorougly checked and rechecked. Anything which is presented as opinion must be very carefully differentiated from that which is presented as fact. A common error made by many beginners is to confuse fact with opinion. So far as is possible readers should be able to 'check' on factual material. However, if they are unable to check on the presented material, they will rely on your ability to interpret and present it correctly in your paper.

Is the material important enough to share with professional colleagues? The relevance of the material to professional practice, administration, research or education should be clear in your mind. Although there is some room in professional journals for articles which have a distinct theoretical basis, those which have an obvious practical application will be valued by editors.

Few of us are able to produce ideas for publication on demand. It is probably best to keep a small file of publishable ideas as they become apparent, and to keep a note of why that particular idea seemed important at the time. Remember, flashes of inspiration can only become pearls of wisdom if they can be recalled at a later stage.

Where to publish

There are a large number and wide range of journals concerned with nursing and related health care subjects, some are highly specialised, many have a very general readership. Because nursing, as with many other professions, is becoming increasingly internationalised there is no need to think of publishing only in your country or language. In order to make decisions about where to publish the article, it may be necessary to visit and consult with a specialist librarian who will be aware of the range of possibilities. A good professional library should contain copies of the relevant journals, and be able to obtain copies of those which are not in stock.

If the article is highly specialised, it will be necessary to choose journals either which deal with that specialty or which have a broad readership. There would be little point in submitting an article about the role of the nurse therapist in treating mastectomy patients to a journal which specialised in the care of patients suffering from infectious diseases. Conversely, almost any article, providing that it is not 'overspecialised', might be submitted to a journal with a general readership.

GUIDES TO CONTRIBUTORS

Once a short list of perhaps three to five journals has been identified as being suitable, the guides which they produce for contributors should be obtained and studied. The 'guides to contributors' are to be found inside every issue of some journals, inside some issues of some journals, or have to be obtained from the editor of others.

The quantity of information which these guides contain will vary considerably among journals. A typical guide will give information about typing requirements, number of copies, length, reference system to be used and the types of illustration which are acceptable. If there are any doubts as to the possible requirements of the journal, even if a guide to contributors has been obtained, further specific questions should be directed to the editor.

In addition, you should examine closely the articles which have appeared in recent issues. By doing so you will get a feel for the type, quality and range of materials which have been acceptable to the journal.

Having considered the contents and requirements of a few selected publications it is necessary next to make a firm decision about the choice of journal. You are now preparing an article with a specific journal in mind rather than having to find a journal to suit the article.

Article structure

The next phase is to develop the idea into a draft structure, the first part of which is to choose a title for the work. Although the title is tentative and may well change as the work progresses, it does serve to give an important focus for, and direction to, the article. The first draft of the major headings to be used should now be written down, they will be produced by 'thinking around' the subject of the article. At this stage there is no need to be too concerned about the order of the ideas, just get them on paper. The major headings can then be rearranged and have the subheadings and sub-subheadings added to them in the same way. Although this structure will be modified as the article progresses, it is a logical starting point from which to work. The major and minor parts of the article should be neither too few nor too many. Too many parts result in a disjointed and difficult to read paper, too few parts and overlong sections may also be difficult and tedious to read.

Example 17 demonstrates how a typical article structure might look.

Finding a publisher

The next task is to find a journal editor who will be willing to give an 'in principle' indication of acceptance. This arrangement will, of course, depend on the acceptability of the final manuscript. However, it does give the writer a fairly firm indication of interest on the part of the editor. If, from your original shortlist of appropriate journals, you find that more than one journal would be suitable to approach, professional courtesy requires that you approach only 'one journal at a time'.

Finding a potential publisher is done by submitting the article structure and by enclosing a covering letter (see Example 18). The letter should be short and to the point, asking for no more than an expression of interest on the part of the editor. Bear in mind that a journal editor may not accept a manuscript until it has been submitted in its entirety. Example 18 illustrates a query letter.

The editor's response to the query letter and enclosed manuscript structure may be one of three: first, a definite expression of interest, in which case you proceed with writing the article;

The Development of Nursing Research

Introduction (No heading required)

The Nature and Purpose of Nursing Research
   The Nature of Nursing Research
      Research Principles
      Universality of research
   The Purpose of Nursing Research
      To advance nursing knowledge
      To confirm current practice
      To identify further research questions

The Development of Nursing Research
   Development in the United Kingdom
      Areas of personal development
      Areas of institutional development

Future Developments
   Government-sponsored Research
      Research fellowships
      Funding of research units
   Privately Funded Research
      Self-supporting research
      Privately commissioned research

Conclusion and Discussion

Example 17   Sample structure of content of article.

second, interest in publishing the manuscript dependent on certain changes being made, in which case you proceed if you wish to comply with these requirements; finally, the editor may reject the proposal on the basis that it 'does not meet with present requirement', in which case you try another journal. Now that the planning phase is complete, work on preparing the full manuscript can begin.

Ward 2
Medical Unit
General Hospital
Finsbury Street
Norman, Worcs
NR2 3GH
England

Date

Mr J.P. Bryant
Editor
<u>Current Nursing Issues</u>
1 Farlane Avenue
Risseville
New Jersey 07623
U.S.A.

Dear Mr Bryant

<u>The Development of Nursing Research</u>

I write to enquire if <u>Current Nursing Issues</u> would be interested in the above manuscript which I am currently preparing. The paper examines the general development of nursing research and speculates about the future direction of this development (see enclosed structure and contents).

The manuscript, which would comply with the editorial requirements of your journal, will be ready for submission approximately three months from this date.

I look forward to hearing from you and hope that you are able to give this proposal your favourable consideration. I shall, of course, be delighted to receive any comments or suggestions you may have regarding the enclosed outline.

Yours sincerely

Name   Qualifications

Enc.

Professional work status
(Staff nurse, for example)

Example 18   Query letter.

WRITING THE ARTICLE

Writing and writing style are a very personal endeavour. At this stage, getting the words on paper is far more important than the achievement of an 'excellent' writing style. Many beginners have difficulty because they (wrongly) believe that there is an 'ideal' writing style to which they should conform. Providing it is clear and readable, your personal writing style should be used. Although there is no universally correct recipe for success in writing the article, the following guidelines are offered.

Research the subject

In this context the word *research* relates to finding out as much as you possibly can about the subject, by reading about the subject, and by discussing it with colleagues. Although you will have chosen the subject because it is of special interest, and because of its relevance to your professional life, there is almost certainly much more information available about it than is realised. By researching the subject, therefore, you are better able to produce an informative, insightful, and well-informed article which will be more satisfying to your readers. Discussing the subject with colleagues plays an important part in the subsequent phases of the writing process.

Obtaining permission

When the contents of the article relate to any identifiable person or institution permission for the material to be published must be obtained. One way of avoiding this issue is to refer to persons as Miss X or Mr Z, or to refer to institutions as 'a district general hospital' for example. Great care must be taken with anonymity, if this cannot be achieved then the permission *must* be obtained.

If any of the ideas or materials referred to, a new handwashing technique for example, have been developed in your place of work then the permission of the employing authority must be obtained. When permission of any kind is being asked the general contents of the article must be made known, and the specific information which relates to the individual or institution must be made available. Ideally, permission should be obtained in writing, verbal permission is sensibly followed by a letter from you acknowledging with thanks the details of the permission granted.

In those instances when permission need not be obtained, where the article makes no reference to your place of work and contains no information about, or reference to, individuals or specific institutions, you may wish to inform others of the intention to publish. At this stage in preparing the manuscript it might be prudent to inform appropriate others, colleagues for example, that the article is being prepared. Once submitted for publication it may also be prudent, particularly if one is working within an organisational structure, to send a copy of the article to senior colleagues 'for information'.

Developing the structure

The previously prepared structure should now be further developed by being examined, rearranged or altered as necessary, and by being extended by the addition of one or more sentences to each of the parts. It is at this stage that you might experience blocks in the writing process. The following hints are intended to minimise these.

Find an environment which is conducive to writing, this varies from person to person and can only be found by experimenting. For some it is the living room in front of the television set, for others it may be their bedroom, for others it may be the college or public library.

Get your thoughts on paper, irrespective of how disorganised they may appear. Remember that perfection may never be achieved, and certainly not in the first draft. Subsequent drafts can be used to rearrange and improve the material.

Always use pages of paper which are the same size, write (pencil is practical) or type on one side of the paper, and always leave large margins around the edges of the paper and in between various sections of the manuscript. This will facilitate 'cutting and pasting' and rearranging the material when doing the next draft.

When writing, ideas relating to both earlier and later parts of the manuscript may emerge. Do not be tempted to go back to the earlier part of the paper, or to commence work on the later stages. However, any ideas which do emerge at this stage should be noted on a piece of paper for use later or for use when writing a subsequent draft.

Think about how the quality of the manuscript might be improved by the use of graphic presentations, that is the use of anything other than words. Make notes of where such illustrations might appear, they can be worked out in detail at a later stage.

Never regard what has been written as unchangeable, subsequent editing will improve the manuscript.

Allow some time to elapse between each draft of the manuscript, a few days may be necessary to allow additional ideas to develop and mature. Ask trusted colleague who are familiar with the subject area to read and comment on each of the drafts. Make full use of a dictionary, thesaurus and an English (or whichever language you are writing in) language textbook.

Article content

In large part the previously determined structure of the article will influence its contents. Thus, if the structure has been well planned, decisions about the contents will be much easier.

It might be useful to think of the article in terms of three major parts which are contained within the over-all structure. They are: the introduction, the body and the conclusion.

INTRODUCTION

The introduction may be regarded as the 'shop window' of the manuscript, not only being the first to be seen but also playing a large part in the decision as to whether the entire paper should be read. The first few sentences of the introduction should capture the readers' attention, and make them wish to read the remainder, it should set the tone for the rest of the paper, and contain a brief outline of the contents.

In general the introduction should be shorter rather than longer, perhaps constituting 10% of the over-all length. Having studied this section the reader should have a fairly clear idea about the contents. Thus, the introduction tells the reader what to expect.

BODY OF THE PAPER

The body of the paper is the longest, most important and may be the most difficult to write. During this phase of writing refer frequently to your previously carefully prepared structure. Indeed, the body of the article emerges from an expansion and elaboration of the structure.

The major problems likely to be encountered at this stage relate to decisions regarding the degree of detail required, ensuring that the paper has a logical sequence, holding the interest of the reader, and maintaining a fluent writing style. The solutions to many of these problems are matters of judgement, with few hard and fast rules applying to them. The best advice that can be given here is that you are critical of your own work, and encourage colleagues to whom the draft copies are shown to be likewise.

CONCLUSION AND DISCUSSION

The principal functions of your third section are to draw the article to a close, summarise its contents, discuss the major features of the paper, and give direction to the possible development of the issues raised. As with all other parts of the paper the concluding section should be carefully planned, written and rewritten.

Further drafts

The process described in the preceding paragraphs is repeated over and over again until the manuscript has been satisfactorily completed. Remember, that although the perfect manuscript has never been prepared, you have the responsibility to write as well as possible. In deciding how many drafts to write there comes a point when the law of diminishing returns applies. Such a point is reached when minimal improvement is to be gained from writing yet another draft. The paper should now be shown to a colleague for final comment before the article is submitted. Before submission, however, it is as well to undertake a thorough presubmission check.

Presubmission check

Check grammar, structure, headings and subheadings, page numbers and length. The article *must* be clear, readable and fluently written. All the requirements of the publisher must be met, any necessary deviations such as reasonable additional length must be made known.

Check the accuracy, content and presentation of all tables, figures and graphs. The title must describe the content of each presentation, they must be referred to in the text close to where they appear, and they must be constructed to achieve maximal impact.

Check the title (does it really describe the contents of the article?) and all other headings, subheadings and sub-subheadings. Examine the sequence and length of all parts of the paper. Check and recheck all references. Do all those cited in the text appear in the reference list? Does the reference system used conform to the journal requirements and is it used correctly and consistently throughout? All quotations in the text must be compared with the publications in which they originated, they must be identical. All items in the reference list must be examined and compared with the original documents or with carefully prepared notes taken from them. The names of the authors, years of publication, titles of publication and all other bibliographical data must be carefully checked and rechecked.

Check that appropriate permission to publish has, if necessary, been obtained, and that this has been confirmed in writing. A copy of the paper should be sent to appropriate colleagues for information.

Check any additional material, other than the actual article, which is to be enclosed. Such materials include acknowledgement of assistance, name (or names) and details of co-author(s), and photographs and other material.

Check the structure and contents of the covering letter which will be enclosed with the article. A covering letter will, of course, always be unique, and its content will be determined by whether there had been previous correspondence, such as an enquiry letter. Example 19 shows a covering letter and is intended to illustrate the points which might usefully be included.

PUBLISHING

If an acknowledgement of receipt of the article has not been obtained by the end of four weeks, although it is reasonable to expect it much sooner, get in touch with the editor by telephone or an additional letter, and ask whether it has been received.

Acceptance and rejection

It is uncommon for articles to be accepted without any suggestions being made or alterations being required. Beginning writers should pay particular attention to this fact, as many are totally devastated and disheartened on being rejected for

Mr J.P. Bryant
Editor
Current Nursing Issues
1 Farlane Avenue
Risseville
New Jersey 07623
U.S.A.

Ward 2
Medical Unit
General Hospital
Finsbury Street
Norman, Worcs
NR2 3GH
England

Date

Dear Mr Bryant

The Development of Nursing Research

In response to your letter of (date) in which you expressed an interest in the above manuscript, I enclose two copies which have been prepared to meet the requirements of Current Nursing Issues.

In order that the manuscript can be placed in the context of my personal experience and professional interests, I enclose a brief curriculum vitae.

I look forward to hearing from you and hope that you will give the manuscript your favourable consideration. I have not, as specified in your Guide to Contributors, submitted the paper to any other journal at present.

Yours sincerely

Name   Qualifications

Encls

Professional work status
(Staff nurse, for example)

Example 19   Covering letter.

whatever reason. However, if the article is accepted then all that is required is that the editor be sent a 'thank you note' and that the subsequent stages of publication of the article be awaited.

The length of time between the acceptance and eventual publication of an article varies considerably from journal to journal. It is unlikely to be published in less than six months, may be published within twelve months and, in some instances, may be published at the end of a two-year period. Although some journals may be willing to give an estimate of the date of publication, most are only willing to say that the article has been 'accepted'.

REJECTION

In the event of an editor rejecting a manuscript which has been submitted for the first time, you must be careful not to respond by either throwing the manuscript in the bucket or by writing an angry letter to the editor. Rejection may be one of two types and will, in each case, have something to teach the writer.

TOTAL REJECTION

Total rejection might take one of two forms. First, the editor may simply refuse to accept the article and include no further comment. Frustrating although this is, it is a fact of life and one which possibly reflects the large number of manuscripts which read the editor's desk. In this case, you should begin to modify the article for submission to another journal.

Some journals give a reason for rejection, for example that it 'does not meet with our present requirement'. Other reasons may be more specific and point to deficiencies in the paper. Any reasons should be studied closely and, if possible, used to improve the article which may be resubmitted to that particular journal or, as is more frequently the case, modified for submission to another.

QUALIFIED REJECTION

Perhaps the most common form of rejection is the one in which the writer is asked to make specific changes in the manuscript before resubmission. If these changes are made to meet the editor's requirements, there is a very good chance that the resubmitted paper will be accepted. Such a request for modification may come from the editor personally, one of the editorial staff of the journal or, as is the case in some nursing journals, from one or two independent referees to whom the manuscript has been sent. Referees are usually asked to comment on the manuscript without knowing the name of the author, the name of the referee making the comments is never sent to the manuscript writer except under exceptional circumstances.

Rejection slips are not the end of the road for a particular manuscript, their contents should be studied carefully and learned from. If the manuscript has reached this stage of development there is an extremely good chance that it will be published providing its writer perseveres.

Writer-editor relationship

Contrary to what some writers believe, editors are friendly people who try hard to enable and encourage professionals to develop their writing skills to the full. They have an obvious vested interest in stimulating the flow of high quality written material, it would not be in their interest to turn down good manuscripts out of hand or to discourage writers with potential. In order to help develop a positive writer-editor relationship it might be worthwhile considering the following points. The development of mutual trust is absolutely essential, requiring both parties to be frank and honest with each other. Writers should expect editors to be totally honest in their opinion about submitted manuscripts, these views should be accepted objectively and professionally, and not interpreted as a personal attack.

Every effort should be made to keep to agreements which have been made, in relation to how long a manuscript will be or when it will be delivered for example.

It is always best to write to the general editor of the journal, or possibly to the specialist editor, by name. This information can usually be found on or near the contents page in a current copy of the journal.

Never submit the same article to more than one journal simultaneously. If, in the unlikely event of multiple submission being absolutely necessary, then this *must* be drawn to the attention of the editor of each of the journals concerned.

Building up a positive working relationship with journal editors can be a profitable and rewarding experience. The fruits of this mutually advantageous personal relationship are undoubtedly better quality manuscripts and increasing publishing opportunities.

Editorial changes

Having accepted the manuscript the editor will subject it to the editing process. All articles are professionally edited and, in my experience, considerably improve the quality of the work. The job of the editor is to improve the work whilst maintaining your writing style, meaning and intention.

The edited manuscript, in the form of proofs, will be returned to you for proofreading. This constitutes a further detailed checking procedure which should take account of the original manuscript and the subsequent editing changes. You must make quite sure that the manuscript contains what you want it to contain, this responsibility rests solely on the writer's shoulders. The checked work, and any corrections, are returned to the editor. If you feel desperately unhappy about any of the editing changes, this should be made known to the editor. Because the editor (of a book or journal) will be working to firm publishing deadlines, the proofs must be returned by the agreed dates, three weeks from the receipt of them not being unusual. If you are to be away from the address to which proofs will be sent for more than two weeks, the editor should be informed.

After publication

When the article is published those who read it are entitled, indeed encouraged, to comment on it. Such comments may take the form of personal correspondence with the writer, letters to the journal in which the article was published, or references to the article in subsequent publications. Remember, these comments can take the form of criticism, congratulations or discussions of its strength and weaknesses. Accept positive comments graciously, learn from critical comments and be slightly concerned about the total absence of any comment whatever.

EXERCISES

Exercises 1—5 are designed to form the basis of developing a manuscript for submission to an editor. The exercises can either be used on a personal basis or form part of a writing-workshop programme.

EXERCISE 1

Identify a topic which will form the basis of an article manuscript. The topic should be stated in such a way so as to form the title of the manuscript.

Write a 500-word essay on the chosen subject.

EXERCISE 2

Prepare a structure which will form the basis of the manuscript. Start with headings, then subheadings, then sub-subheadings. Write two or three sentences in relation to each of the parts of the structure.

EXERCISE 3

Combine the materials prepared in Exercises 1 and 2 to form the first draft of the manuscript. A possible target length at this stage might be 1,000 words.

EXERCISE 4

Identify one or more journals to which submission of this type of manuscript might be appropriate. Obtain, either from the journal or by writing to the editor, a copy of the guide to contributors from each journal.

EXERCISE 5

Ask a colleague who is a familiar with the subject area to read and comment on the manuscript. Bear these comments in mind when preparing a subsequent draft.

Having reached this stage or preparation, you should think seriously about finishing the work on the manuscript and submitting it for publication.

Chapter 11
Books

Although writing a book requires the same range of skills and experience as are required to write an article, book authors must apply those skills and experience to provide a much wider and deeper coverage of the subject matter. Those who are beginning a career in nursing should give serious thought to developing a confidence in the skills and knowledge they acquire to dispel any future doubts about writing a book. All the preceding, and some subsequent, chapters contain material which is relevant to the preparation of a book, in particular the chapter on writing articles, and the chapter dealing with proofreading and preparing an index. In the interest of brevity repetition of pertinent facts will be kept to a minimum.

Although nursing and other professions are becoming increasingly reliant on the use of articles and audio-visual aids for educational and other purposes, the textbook continues to play a key role in the dissemination of professional knowledge. In some parts of the world these textbooks, even nursing textbooks, are written by individuals who are not members of the profession for whom the books are intended. In the United Kingdom, for example, many 'nursing' textbooks were written solely by doctors of medicine up until the mid-1960s. Although the very important contribution of non-nurses to the development of nursing literature is recognised, the fact that nursing as a profession is now producing its own textbook literature is to be welcomed.

The decision to write a book can be arrived at in two distinct ways: the idea can be publisher- or writer-initiated.

Publisher-initiated books

Publishers and their specialist editors are constantly inviting nurses to identify areas in which books require to be written. For this reason they travel around colleges, schools of nursing and areas in which nurses work, in order to establish where the gaps in the professional literature are. Having received confirmation from various sources that a particular book is needed, the next task of the publisher is to find someone to write it. Publishers also encourage their staff to make and maintain contact with potential book writers, and identify the specialist areas of these potential writers.

When publishers have ascertained that there is a need for a particular book, they will then contact a potential writer for it and, if the invitation to write is accepted, then the book will appear on the bookshelf in due course. In some instances the publisher may have to 'shop around' to find a suitable writer.

At this time the demand for book authors far outweighs the number of people who are willing and able to undertake such a task. Such is the shortage of potential authors that all publishers are more than happy to receive proposals from potential writers.

Writer-initiated books

Prospective authors who feel that there is a definite need for a book on a particular subject are encouraged to contact a publisher and offer to write the book. Such proposals are, of course, tentative in the first instance and never commit either party: much groundwork has to be done before any formal contract stage is reached.

As with an article, preparing a book has a number of distinct phases; these are planning, writing and publishing.

PLANNING A BOOK

The idea that a book is required frequently arises from the belief that, although such a book is necessary, it does not already exist within the present range of professional texts. This gap in the literature might be recognised by a teacher, clinician, administrator or researcher, underlining the fact that all four groups have a responsibility to produce an appropriate literature. Alternatively, the need for a particular textbook might arise from the belief that the present range of books is inadequate.

Confirming the idea

The notion that the book is required must be confirmed by making a thorough examination of the existing textbooks on the subject, and deciding whether the subject is adequately covered. This review of the existing literature will have to be discussed with a prospective publisher in due course, for obvious reasons it is as well to do this earlier rather than later. Having identified a gap in the literature, you should discuss the need for the text with colleagues who are familiar with the subject area. These discussions will help you anticipate the responses which a publisher might receive when obtaining similar opinions on the need for the book from other professionals.

If, having searched the literature and found it to be wanting and having the need for such a text confirmed by colleagues, you wish to continue with the idea then the next task is to select a publisher.

Selecting a publisher

A look through the bookshelves in a college or nursing library will reveal that a relatively small number of publishers deal with nursing texts. It is as well to identify three or four publishers who produce good quality nursing texts and who are reasonably accessible by letter and telephone. A short letter should be sent to each of the publishers asking them for a copy of advice and/or guidelines which they have for prospective authors. At this stage, the letter should contain no information or details about the proposed text. In short, you are in the process of choosing a publisher rather than vice versa.

The replies which are received by you may or may not contain additional information which will help in the selection of a publisher. On being contacted in the way described, publishers will invariably ask for details about the proposed book so that they can decide whether or not to accept the proposal. Although the type of information requested by publishers will vary, I have selected a sampling to give some indication of the type and range of questions. The notes following each question have been prepared by me and would not form part of the questionnaire sent out by publishers.

QUESTIONNAIRE SENT TO PROSPECTIVE AUTHOR

Q.1 *What is the aim and general purpose of the book?*

Notes A provisional title and a brief description of the aim and scope of the book should be provided. A draft chapter outline will indicate the scope of the book. The structure should be carefully arranged with each chapter title being descriptive of its contents. It is strongly recommended that a few sentences be used to describe the content of each chapter.

Q.2 *For which readership is the book intended?*

Notes A clear statement of the intended readership should be made. For example, this might be 'all nurses in training for a register', 'all nurses training for the psychiatric register', 'all undergraduate nurses', 'nursing assistants' or 'all trained nurses'. Any other groups who might find the book of value should be mentioned including, for example, medical staff, psychologists, social workers, physiotherapists, occupational therapists and radiographers.

Q.3 *Will the book be of particular interest to any nursing courses? If so, might it be used as a compulsory text or as a reference text?*

Notes Bear in mind that publishing is a commercial business and that books which have a very narrow potential readership are less attractive to publishers than those which have a wider audience. Clearly, a text which may be of use to a very small number of highly specialised nurses is a less practical proposition as far as the publisher is concerned. Indeed, you may well wish to consider extending the scope of the book to make it more likely to be used by a wider readership. In order to answer this question well, prospective authors require a good understanding of nursing generally, not just of their own specialty. In this way the most realistic and convincing answer to the question can be provided. If there is any doubt about the range of courses which might find this book of use, then it might be as well to discuss this point with colleagues from other nursing disciplines.

Q.4 *What is the anticipated length of the book and is it likely to include illustrations in the form of photographs, line drawings, tables and figures?*

Notes Even at this early stage in the development of the book, some estimate needs to be made of its possible length. This may be achieved by reexamination of the chapter titles and by roughly estimating the word length of each chapter. Whichever estimate is made there is room for subsequent revision, but it should be as near as can be achieved, for example to the nearest 10,000 words. (As a guide, this book contains approximately 60,000 words, 320 words per page.) The use of and number of illustrations also needs to be estimated, bearing in mind that this will be provisional. Some texts, for example those relating to anatomy and physiology, will require many illustrations. Others, such as psychiatric texts, may require few or none at all.

Q.5 *What is the intended completion date for the manuscri, t?*

Notes The answer will depend on personal circumstances, previous experience of writing and available time. However, in the absence of any better means of making an estimate, it is suggested that the reply be '18 months from the date of signing the contract'.

Q.6 *Which other books will compete with the proposed text? If there are competitors, describe why you feel the proposed book to be necessary.*

Notes Prior to answering this question it will be necessary to have made a thorough search of the existing book literature on the subject. Any competition identified, however weak or strong, must be made known. Publishers realise that a variety of books on a given subject should be available, so acknowledging the existence of competition will not automatically cause the proposal to be rejected. If any books are identified in response to this question, then all details, in the form of a formal reference, should be made available.

Q.7 *Please give full details of previous professional experience, professional qualifications and other relevant information.*

Notes As with other responses, this reply should be well thought out and well-written. It should contain full details of past experience, qualifications, courses attended, publications, special honours, special interests and membership of any professional committees or societies. This general answer to the question will be followed by a much more detailed description of those items which refer to the subject of the book. For example, if the subject of the book is surgical nursing then all items relating to that area of experience and expertise should be discussed in full. In response to this question other professionals would simply reply 'see enclosed curriculum vitae'. However, many nurses are either not aware of the need to construct such a document or (wrongly) feel that their experience and expertise are not important enough to form the subject of a curriculum vitae.

All nurses should pay more attention to this means of assuring credibility, and to doing this by means of using their writing skills to maximum advantage. Constructing a well-written and neatly presented curriculum vitae is essential for those who wish to contribute to the professional literature. It is usual to be requested to provide a curriculum vitae when submitting a manuscript or when establishing if a publisher is interested in a potential manuscript.

Because of the importance of preparation, and because it constitutes an important part of the answer to this question asked by the publisher, a possible curriculum vitae outline is presented in Example 20.

The outline contains *examples* of the type of materials which should be included. Although nurses are often reluctant to publicise their strength, achievements, distinctions and range of experience, but this must be done fully and honestly in a curriculum vitae.

The carefully prepared answers to the questionnaire, the outline of the book, the curriculum vitae and (preferably) a sample chapter should be sent to the publisher along with a short covering letter.

Publisher's decision

Publishers will weigh up the evidence very carefully before deciding whether the proposal is a viable one It will be looked at from a commercial and literary viewpoint by editorial staff, including those who are also nurses if the publisher employs such staff. It may also be examined by independent referees to whom the outline will be sent. The role of independent referee in influencing the decision to accept or reject the proposal is crucial. The types of question which the referees will be asked by the publisher are fully discussed in Chapter 13.

If the publisher's reply is negative, reasons for the rejection

Page	Contents	
Front page	Personal details	Name
		Qualifications
		Date of birth
1	Contents page	This page will list all further contents and page numbers of the curriculum vitae.
2	List of professional qualifications	List each qualification. Brief description of each. Year of completion. Place qualifications obtained.
3	Details of work experience (including present post)	Give title of each position (e.g. staff nurse). Place and dates of employment. Major responsibilities associated with each.
4	Courses attended (including study days, conferences and formal post-registration courses)	Itemise courses attended. Date. Brief description of each.
5	Papers presented at courses, conferences, study days, etc.	Title of paper. Date of presentation. Name of conference etc.

Example 20 Outline curriculum vitae.

6	Publications	List all app-ropriate pub-lications. Give full ref-erence to each.
7	Research experience	Personal research. Research parti-cipation. Research con-sultancy (Give brief details of each).
8	Membership of appropriate organisations, committees and working parties	Give brief details of each.
9	Distinctions and awards	List and give brief details of all awards, honours, scholar-ships etc.
10	Any other appropriate information	Editorial panel member. Publishing con-sultancy. Book reviewing.

may or may not be included. In either case the reply and its implications should be carefully considered prior to contacting another publisher. It may be that an otherwise excellent idea is not commercially viable in that the numbers of potential buyers is too small. The options open to you at this stage are either to 'push ahead' with the proposal and direct it to another pub-lisher, to revise it before resubmission, or to abandon it. The remainder of this section will assume that the proposal has been accepted by a publisher.

THE CONTRACT

The publisher will prepare and send two copies of a contract to the author with a request that both copies be signed and returned for the publisher's signature. When the publisher has countersigned both copies, one copy will be returned to the author.

The contract should be carefully studied before it is signed by the author, it constitutes a legal document which is binding on both parties. Although it has been prepared by the publisher, it *is* open to negotiation before signing. Contracts vary among publishers, but there are many similarities. A typical publisher's contract contains a number of clauses related to the 'life' of the work. Do not be reluctant to ask questions if something is not clear, to discuss it with your solicitor, or to suggest alterations.

Contract title contains terms such as 'memorandum of agreement' or 'an agreement' followed by the date on which the contract was prepared, name and full details of the author, and name and full details of the publishing company.

Details of book relates to its title, which may well be tentative, and its approximate length. Although the stated length is approximate, any deviation from this by more than 10% should be discussed with the publisher. Firm details of the submission date of the manuscript will be included.

Costs of publishing, which will be met in full by the publisher, are detailed.

Sole publishing rights will be given to the publisher who is included in the contract. This part of the agreement prevents the author from continuing or initiating discussions with any other publisher in connection with this particular book.

Existing copyright and libel needs to be considered by the author. By signing the contract he/she assures the publisher that the contents of the book do not infringe any existing copyright, nor does it contain anything which is libelous, obscene or indecent.

Advertising and production arrangements will be left to the discretion of the publisher: this includes the distribution of free and review copies, and decisions about the form of the binding, jacket and cover of the book. In short the publisher will take full responsibility for advertising this work and making it sell.

Illustrations and diagrams will be supplied by the author and at the author's cost.

Proof stage alterations must be kept to a minimum and will only be paid for by the publisher if the cost of any such alterations are no greater than a percentage (usually 10%) of the original cost of composing the type of the manuscript. It is important that the author keep any changes in the manuscript to an absolute minimum following its initial submission to the publisher. The author must further agree to read, check and correct all proofs of the manuscript and to return them to the publisher within an agreed time.

Additional editorial work may be completed by the publisher's editorial staff or may be commissioned by them. If the publisher has to employ an editor to do this work, the costs may have to be paid for by the author. However, any such arrangements, including costs, will be fully discussed with the author in advance.

The index to the work will be prepared by the author or by a person employed by him/her, or by the publisher at the author's expense.

Copyright allocation may be made to the publisher as part of the contract. If not, then the copyright remains the property of the author.

Subsequent editions of the work will require to be edited and revised by the author. This section may discuss the conditions which will apply in the event of the death of the author.

Royalties are stated in one of several ways; first, as a percentage of the published price; as a percentage of the price paid by booksellers to the publishers, or as a set fee per thousand copies printed. For a fuller discussion of royalties see Chapter 15.

Serialisation and translation offers made to the publisher will be fully discussed with the author prior to acceptance or rejection. Any sums paid in respect of the sale of such rights may be shared equally between the author and publisher.

Free copies, ranging from between 5 and 25, may be given to the author. In most instances the author will be able to purchase further copies for personal use at a discount off the published price.

The right to refuse to publish, in the event of the manuscript not meeting the required standards, will be retained by the publisher.

Publisher bankruptcy and publisher author disagreements may be dealt with in the concluding sections of the contract. In the event of the publisher becoming bankrupt, the right to print and publish the work may revert to the author. The means of resolving any disagreement between author and publisher may be specified, for example that the matter shall be referred to the arbitration of two persons, one to be named by each party.

Although contracts may, at first sight, seem unnecessarily long and complicated, they are relatively easy to understand providing that each of the parts is read carefully. Should there be any real difficulty in understanding a contract, it should never be signed before it is fully discussed with someone with a knowledge of the subject. For example, it might be discussed with a friend who works for another publishing company. Alternatively, it might be discussed with a colleague who has publishing experience, and experience of contracts. Finally, it may be prudent to discuss the contents of the contract with a lawyer.

WRITING THE BOOK

The time taken to write a book will vary considerably depending on the amount of previous preparation, the writing skills of the author and the extent to which the ideas for the book have been allowed to mature and develop. As was suggested earlier in this chapter, it is as well to set a date for the final manuscript which is eighteen months away from the date of signing the contract. At this stage you should begin to prepare a firm timetable of events relating to writing the book. For example, if there are twelve major sections or chapters in the book, the time allocation might be as follows: three months for further planning of the work, for research and for making detailed notes about each of its parts; twelve months for writing the twelve chapters, a month per chapter; and three months for 'putting the book together' and for thoroughly checking every item in it.

Publisher's guide for authors

Most publishers prepare a guide for their authors, if this has not already been obtained it should be requested immediately.

Understandably, the guidelines are fairly general and relate to structure and presentation rather than to contents. The following eleven guidelines are typical of those which may be sent by a publisher.

PRESENTATION OF MANUSCRIPT

Type the final copy on one side of A4 paper, use double-spacing and leave 3.8 cm ($1\frac{1}{2}$inch) margin at all sides. Prepare three copies, send the top copy and the second copy to the publisher and retain the third. Number the pages in the manuscript in sequence throughout, this includes appendices and reference list. All tables and figures must be referred to in the text at a point very close to which they are presented. The agreed chapter and manuscript length must be closely adhered to. All minor corrections must be legible and clearly made in the text or indicated and made in the margin. Lengthy corrections should be typed on a separate A4 sheet and keyed to their place and page number.

STYLE

Advice on the use of abbreviations, symbols, metrication, numbers and means of referring to figures and tables may be given here. For example, you might be advised to use 'per cent' in the text but the symbol % in the tables. Advice may also be given on the use of drug names, the approved name being most commonly required. Any points of style which are not referred to in this section, but which need to be discussed, should be raised with the publisher.

USE OF ITALICS

The use of italics, or the use of underlining if the typewriter does not have an italic facility, should be clarified. For example, foreign words, the titles of books and journals, and quotations may be italicised.

SPECIMEN PRESENTATION

A short example of how material should be presented may be included. This example will probably be used to highlight the important points and problem areas.

ILLUSTRATIONS

Clear instructions as to the use of illustrations, whether they be photographs, line drawings or other forms of illustration, must be obtained. Most publishers have specific requirements in relation to these and are unable to use anything which does not meet them.

HEADINGS

Headings are used to make the text more readable and visually attractive. With the chapter heading, which is a major heading, three or four subsidiary headings may be used. Whether or not the typewriter has the facility to print headings of the different required sizes, it is normal practice to indicate the grade or weight of the heading in the margin to the left. For example, if the heading is the major or primary heading size then the encircled number 1 or letter A will be placed to the left of that heading. Similarly, if the heading is the least weight or grade then an encircled number 4 or a D will be placed to the left.

REFERENCES

Authors must expect a clear indication of the form of reference style to be used in the manuscript. In addition to indicating the style to be used, the guide should contain some examples of how the references should be used and presented.

FOOTNOTES

In general footnotes are discouraged but, if they are essential, they should be placed on separate sheets at the end of the manuscript with an indication of the page number on which they should appear.

PROOFS

A brief indication of the arrangements for proofreading the manuscript may be included. It is usual for more detailed instructions regarding the proofreading process to be sent to you along with the proofs.

INDEX

Although the need for constructing an index may be mentioned at this stage, serious work on it cannot begin until after completion of the manuscript. It is usual for full instructions regarding the compilation of an index to be sent at a later stage.

SUBMITTING THE MANUSCRIPT

Details of how to package and send the manuscript and to whom it should be addressed may be included.

WRITING

The principles which were discussed in earlier parts of this book, in relation to an article or research report for example, also apply to writing a book. The content and structure of individual chapters require careful attention as will the relationship of one chapter to all others. Individual chapters constitute the general structure of the book, requiring to be placed in the best possible sequence. Indeed, there is little more that can be said about writing a chapter that has not already been said elsewhere in this book.

There are, however, features of a book structure which are unique to it and which will rarely be found in other areas of writing. Although these additional items need not be written until work has ended on all the chapters, they will have to be taken account of, or referred to, during chapter writing.

Foreword

Many books contain a foreword which is a short introductory section, written by an authority on the subject who has been invited to do so, and which is placed at the front of the book. The foreword is traditionally written in a positive and complimentary vein, seeking to draw the reader's attention to the positive aspects of the book.

Preface or prologue

The preface is a short introductory section which has been written by the author. Although its major function is to present the aim and intent of the text in a general manner, it also frequently incorporates the acknowledgement of assistance of those who helped make the book possible. Otherwise, the acknowledgements constitute their own section.

Dedication

On occasions, the author will dedicate the book to a person, institution or belief. The form of the dedication will vary considerably but may take one of the following:

'This book is dedicated to my husband and family'

or

'This book is dedicated to my teachers'

or

This book is dedicated to the future development of the nursing profession'

Other elements of the structure which are considered to be 'optional' and about which decisions for inclusion need to be made are: a bibliography, a glossary, reading lists and practical exercises.

PUBLISHING

When the manuscript has been submitted to the publishers they will edit it and may return it to the author for review and approval, or they may have it set in galley proof or page proof form. In either event the material *will be* returned to you for checking. The tedious task of manuscript review or proofreading requires considerable time, effort and accuracy. The job of the author is to check every word, every sentence and every heading of the work to make absolutely sure that it is correct in meaning, style and presentation. When this time-consuming task has been done the manuscript or proof is returned to the publishers with the relevant corrections having been made. This subject is more fully discussed in the next chapter. One point, however, that should be borne in mind at *all* stages is keeping the publisher informed in advance of any changes of address (personal and professional) and any extended absence from those addresses (holidays, temporary repostings). It serves no purpose having manuscripts, or proofs—or worse a royalty cheque—sitting on an empty desk or 'floating' about the post office in search of the addressee.

Although the publishers have the sole responsibility for publishing the text, and for maximising its commercial success, they may look to you for assistance in relation to this latter function. Because you are particularly knowledgeable about the subject of the text, you may be asked for information which will help in promoting it. For example, you may be asked to suggest journals to which review copies of the book might be sent. Similarly, you might be asked for the names of nursing groups, conferences or societies who should be informed of the existence of the work. You will be asked to participate in the publicity of the book by making available information about your experience, background and interest in the subject. On occasions the 'author's questionnaire' which is sent to authors by the publicity department is quite lengthy and detailed. Personal data can be extracted from the curriculum vitae, but an author's active awareness of national and international conferences scheduled for near publication time will be useful information for a publicity department.

Developing an idea into a published book is a long and difficult task. It requires a thorough understanding of the subject area and a complete commitment to it. However, despite the painfulness of the experience, 'giving birth' to a book can be a particularly rewarding endeavour, and one which all nurses should consider.

EDITING A BOOK

An increasing number of books are 'edited' rather than written by one or two authors. In this context the function of a general editor is to contact a number of writers, each of whom will contribute one or more chapters to the book. The general editor, who will also contribute to the book, plays a major part in coordinating the efforts of all the contributors, ensuring the over-all quality and continuity of the work and making decisions about the sequence of the contributions. An editor will also examine, and if necessary edit, all contributions to ensure that each of the parts are consistent in quality, style and level of presentation.

Whether producing a book as an author or general editor, it is essential that you form and maintain a good working relationship with the appropriate member of publishing staff. Invariably the publishing company will assign one of its staff to work with you, this relationship continuing from start to finish. You should feel free, indeed be encouraged, to get in touch with the publisher with any questions regarding production of the book.

Any difficulties which are being experienced should be reported to the publisher. For example, if agreed deadlines are not to be met, because of illness or other similar reasons, the publisher should be contacted immediately.

If you have an idea for a book and feel you are the person to write it, do not hesitate to get in touch with a possible publisher. They are, after all, in the business of publishing books and will be delighted to hear from you.

EXERCISES

Exercises 1—5 are designed to help identify a possible idea for a book, to confirm the need, and to help develop an outline for the text. The exercises can either be used on a personal basis or form part of a writing workshop.

EXERCISE 1

Prepare an annotated bibliography of at least five books in your subject area. In writing the annotations to each of the books try answer the questions 'What are the strengths and weaknesses of this book?' 'Does it really meet the needs of people who use it?'.

EXERCISE 2

Identify, perhaps as a result of preparing the annotated bibliography, a subject about which you feel a book should be written. Discuss your ideas with colleagues and see if they confirm your ideas about the need for the book. If you are still convinced of the need for the book, write a one-page essay outlining this gap in the literature. Write a second essay outlining the possible range and contents of your 'ideal' book on the subject.

EXERCISE 3

Prepare a structure for this book, identifying each of the chapter titles and writing a few sentences in relation to each.

EXERCISE 4

Write a draft of one of the chapters, perhaps one quarter of its anticipated length.

EXERCISE 5

Imagine you have approached a publisher with regard to your authorship of the book and have been sent a questionnaire similar to the one described earlier in this chapter. Answer each of the questions as convincingly as possible.

Now that you have reached this stage in identifying and developing an idea for a book, you might seriously consider pursuing it.

Chapter 12
Manuscript Checking, Proofreading and Indexing

CHECKING

Having prepared the final draft of the manuscript, be it an article or a book, you must thoroughly check it before submitting it to the publisher. At this stage the contents, in terms of presentation, layout, accuracy and meaning should have been closely examined prior to having this final draft typed in double spacing with wide margins. However, a further verification of the typed manuscript is absolutely essential before sending it off. Although radical changes are highly unlikely at this stage, a surprisingly large number of minor alterations may be necessary.

All corrections and alterations should be incorporated clearly and legibly into the typescript. It might be prudent to 'try out' these alterations and corrections in pencil before using ink. This way, you can confirm that the space available for the corrections is large enough; also, for style changes the publisher may suggest that the original statement was more effective and recommend restoring it — an easier reversal will be accomplished with an eraser.

Example 21 shows how part of a manuscript requiring corrections might appear, it is followed by the same material (Example 22) which has been retyped in order to demonstrate how the corrections will be incorporated by the publisher.

PAGE NUMBERING

Until the manuscript is about to be sent to the publisher, all page numbers should be in pencil. The advantage of pencil is that page numbers can be changed if pages are added to or subtracted from the total length of the manuscript.

If the numbers have been typed on to the manuscript and changes need to be made, it as well to use the following method. If pages have to be added, then they should be placed as appropriate and their numbers should become continuous with those

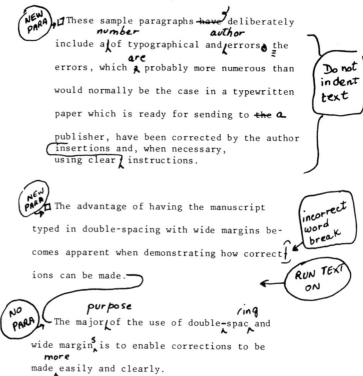

Example 21 Manuscript requiring corrections.

of the original pages of the manuscript which precede the addition. For example, if five new pages are to be added between pages 9 and 10 they would be numbered: 9a, 9b, 9c, 9d, 9e. At the top of page 9, an encircled note stating: 'Followed by pages 9a—9e' is helpful. If pages have to be removed from the manuscript this should be done by removing the appropriate pages and by leaving the numbers on the original pages intact. For example, if pages 95 and 96 are removed then an encircled note at the top of page 94 stating: 'Pages 95 and 96 have been omitted' will alert the publisher. An additional mention that pages 95 and 96 have been removed from the manuscript in your covering letter to the publisher will ensure notice.

When checking the manuscript it is easy, bearing in mind you may have read it many times before, to overlook obvious

These sample paragraphs deliberately include

a number of typographical and author errors. The

errors, which are probably more numerous than

would normally be the case in a typewritten

paper which is ready for sending to a publisher,

have been corrected by the author using clear

insertions and, when necessary, instructions.

The advantage of having the manuscript

typed in double-spacing with wide margins be-

comes apparent when demonstrating how correc-

tions can be made. The major purpose of the

use of double-spacing and wide margins is to

enable corrections to be made more easily and

clearly.

Example 22 Corrected manuscript.

errors in it. When making this final check, it is best to read the
manuscript aloud in order to detect errors in meaning as well as
typographical errors. If possible, get a colleague to listen to you
reading the manuscript aloud.

No matter how well you have checked a manuscript, particularly long ones, errors of style, content and presentation will
be picked up by the publisher. In addition to discovering these
errors, the publisher's printer may introduce errors when
transcribing the manuscript into print. For the reason, the
publisher will submit proofs to you for reading and correcting.

PROOFREADING

The publisher sends proof copies of the manuscript to the writer
for checking for factual or typographical errors. Although some
publishers will permit a minimal amount of alterations to the

work to be made at this stage, bear in mind that these can be costly, particularly in page proof, to the publisher and that the writer may be held financially responsible if these exceed the predetermined percentage.

There is another aspect of excessive alterations to proof which every writer should remember: each additional charge to the cost of producing a book will eventually affect the final selling price of that book. If your book is addressed to a 'price-sensitive' market, that is a limited spending audience, you may well be pricing your work above your readers' pockets with alterations that should have been attended to in the manuscript stage.

The proof copy should be compared with the original typescript, a copy of which, bearing all emendations, should have been retained by the author. It is difficult to overemphasise the need for concentration, accuracy and care when reading proofs. Ideally, you should read the proofs aloud to a colleague who should compare that material with the content of the original typewritten manuscript. In doing so, it is essential that everything be read and compared, every full stop, every comma, every dash, every word and so on. In short *everything* which will appear on the published page must be checked.

The corrections which are to be made on the proofs may take one of two forms, depending on the type of instructions which have been received from the publisher. Occasionally, the publisher will simply request that clear and legible corrections be made in the margin. The format of these corrections will be similar to those made on the typewritten pages prior to submission of the manuscript. Alternatively, the publisher may include a list of recognised 'proof correction marks' (see Example 23) which you should use in the margin and text in order to indicate items requiring correction. Although the proof correction marks used by publishers may vary, those shown in Example 23 (used by the publisher of this book) are typical of many. In this example of proof marks, the publisher has requested that the author use different colours of ink to indicate printer's errors and personal alterations. The material in the left column is *not* entered onto the proof, only the symbols in the middle and right columns are used. Whether or not proof marks are to be used, the important point is that both the publisher and the author have the same understanding of whichever marks are used.

Having sent out the proofs for checking the publisher will wish to have them returned as quickly as possible, within two weeks for example. Because of the time scale within which the publisher is now working, it is essential that every effort be made to comply with such a request. If there is any anticipated delay, if you expect to be on holiday for example, then this should have been made known to the publishers well in advance and possible alternative arrangements made.

INDEXING

An index is an alphabetical list of names or subjects, together with the page numbers on which they appear in the text, which is usually placed at the end of the publication if it is in book form. There are two common types of index which might be used: an author index and a subject index.

Author Index

An author index may be necessary if the book contains a large number of references to other people's works. Thus, if a reader of the book wishes to establish on which pages references to the work of a particular author appears, he/she will find those pages set against the name of the author in the index where they are alphabetically listed. This type of index is more frequently found, and is perhaps of greatest use, in scholarly or research-based texts.

Many texts combine their author index with their subject index, others make no reference to authors cited in the book, but rely upon the reference section for information retrieval.

Subject Index

The subject index is an alphabetical list, using entries, sub-entries and sub-subentries, to indentify the contents of the book. The subject index, which is clearly far more detailed than the list of contents placed at the front of the book, will include items of relevance which are mentioned either briefly or extensively in the text.

The cost of preparing the index is usually borne by the author of the book. It may be prepared by the author, or prepared by a professional indexer hired by the publisher. If the

Any errors in this proof which have been noticed by the printer's reader have been marked in green. If you see any more printer's errors, please mark them in red; there is no charge for correcting these mistakes. For your own alterations, please use black or blue or any colour other than green or red. Please use the proof correction marks shown below for all alterations and corrections.

Instruction to printer	Textual mark	Marginal mark
Leave unchanged	. . . under matter to remain	⊘
Insert in text the matter indicated in the margin	⋏	New matter followed by ⋏
Delete	⊢⊣ through matter to be deleted	∫
Delete and close up	⊜ through matter to be deleted	∫̑
Substitute character or substitute part of one or more word(s)	/ through letter or ⊢⊣ through word	New letter or new word
Change to italics	___ under matter to be changed	⎣⎦
Change to capitals	≡ under matter to be changed	≡
Change to small capitals	= under matter to be changed	=
Change to bold type	⌵⌵⌵ under matter to be changed	⌵⌵⌵
Change to bold italic	⌵⌵⌵ under matter to be changed	⌵⌵⌵
Change to lower case	Encircle matter to be changed	≢
Change italic to upright type	[As above]	⎣⏋
Insert 'superior' character	/ through character or ⋏ where required	⅄ under character, e.g. ⅄
Insert 'inferior' character	[As above]	⋏ over character, e.g. ⋏
Insert full stop	[As above]	⊙
Insert comma	[As above]	,
Insert single quotation marks	[As above]	⌇ and/or ⌇
Insert double quotation marks	[As above]	⌇⌇ and/or ⌇⌇
Insert hyphen	[As above]	⊢⊣
Start new paragraph	⌐⌐	⌐⌐
No new paragraph	⊃	⊃
Transpose	⎣⏋	⎣⏋
Close up	linking ⊃ letters	⊃
Insert space between letters		between letters affected	Y
Insert space between words		Y between words affected	Y
Reduce space between letters		between letters affected	↑
Reduce space between words	↑ between words affected	↑

BLACKWELL SCIENTIFIC PUBLICATIONS
Example 23 Proof correction marks.

publishers hire an indexer, they will pay for the indexing and deduct the cost from the first royalty payment to the author.

If the index is prepared by a professional indexer, whether he/she is hired by the author or publisher, it is *essential* that the author read the index manuscript. It is possible that the author will be able to correct errors in the index, and add to its general quality by virtue of his/her knowledge of the subject matter.

Professional indexer fees can be expensive, and the author's knowledge of the text is a considerable advantage in personally preparing an index. Many writers, therefore, successfully undertake this task themselves. If you decide to compile your own index, seek the publisher's advice, and request any publishing guides to or list of literature on preparing an index.

Because preparing an index is something which cannot be fully completed until after page proofs have been received from the publisher, it is often left until the last minute or, worse still not included in a very small number of texts. To avoid a 'last minute' rush it is advisable to start work on an index as early as possible. For example, the amended copy of the manuscript which is retained by you can be used to underline those words or terms which are likely to be included in the index. These should then be transferred onto index cards, alphabetically filed and subsequently rearranged into index entries, subentries and sub-subentries. The index can in fact be prepared, although the page numbers on which each item appears can only be added when page proofs are received from the publisher.

The question of indexing should be raised with the publisher as soon as possible and decision made with regard to its length, whether it will be a subject or author or combined index, and who will prepare it. If it is to be prepared by the author, who might have no previous indexing experience, then, as mentioned before, assistance should be requested from the publisher and appropriate professional texts should be used as an indexing guide.

EXERCISES

Exercises 1—2 have been designed to facilitate the development of skills in relation to checking and proofreading a manuscript, and in relation to constructing an index. The exercises can either be used on a personal basis or form part of a writing-workshop programme.

EXERCISE 1

Write a 300-word essay on any subject and include a considerable number of intentional errors. Have the essay typed in double-spacing with wide margins on all sides. Check the typewritten essay and make the necessary corrections using ink. Ask a colleague to read the corrected essay to you and judge whether he/she has been able to understand your corrections. Remember, if corrections are misunderstood it is the fault of the person making the corrections, not the fault of the reader.

EXERCISE 2

Select and read an article from a professional journal. Underline each item in the article which you feel might constitute an index entry. Construct an index for the article using entries, subentries and sub-subentries. Each index entry must include, and preferably begin with, a noun.

An example of how entry, subentry and sub-subentry may be used is:

Nursing   1—5
  general   1
  psychiatric   3—5
    community   3
    institution   4

Chapter 13
Publishing Consultancies

Among other publishing-related opportunities available to writers in many professions is consultancy work. This stems from the need some publishing companies have to employ specialists, either on a part-time or on an ad hoc basis. In medical and nursing publishing particularly, this need arises from the publisher's responsibility to ensure absolute accuracy in the life-pertaining facts contained within a textbook; and, in another vein, to keep informed of development and changes of method or approach with the profession it serves.

Traditionally, consultancy work has resulted from individual nurses being contacted by publishers. However, publishers new to the field welcome, indeed encourage, nurses to get in touch with them and discuss possible contribution.

Although marginally different qualities may be required of nurses who are involved in different types of consultancy work, similar qualities are required of all who are involved in this aspect of the publishing business. A thorough knowledge of the subject matter of the work is certainly required. Honesty and integrity are of considerable importance, bearing in mind that the material received at a prepublication stage is highly confidential. Similarly, the consultant may be required to give a full and frank opinion of the professional authenticity of work, an opinion which may be positive or negative. The consultant is frequently requested to work to a fixed deadline, and should accept the work only if it is certain that it can be completed in the agreed time. The ability to review objectively the quality of a given piece is essential, and requires you to be thoroughly familiar with the subject for constructive criticism. Finally, a clear and succinct writing style is required for this type of work.

A selection of the more commonly used consultancies are presented along with some notes on what might be expected by a publisher. Remember that considerable variation exists with regard to this work.

PUBLISHING CONSULTANCIES (BOOKS)

Book publishers are the major consumers of consultancy services. The services involve book proposals, submitted manuscripts and sometimes published books.

Book proposals

Having received information regarding a proposed book from a prospective author, the publisher will first do market research and, when this is positive, will then undertake a detailed discussion of the proposal with a consultant who will act as a 'referee'.

The following nine questions are typical of those which may be sent to a referee along with details of the proposal. The notes following each question have been prepared by me for readers of this text, and would not form part of the questionnaire sent out by publishers.

QUESTIONNAIRE SENT TO BOOK PROPOSAL REFEREE

Q.1 *Is there a need for this type of book?*

Notes You will require to be thoroughly familiar with the subject matter and with the existing literature on it in order to answer this question. Publishers are aware of the universal scope of nursing, and of the need for the literature to have an international appeal. Some attempt should be made to answer this question in relation to an international readership.

If books on the subject already exist, including those which are published abroad, the value of an additional book on the subject needs to be carefully considered. However, if the existing books have deficiencies which the proposed book does not have, then this should be drawn to the publisher's attention.

Q.2 *What are the major competitors to this book?*

Notes Publishers will look to you to use your knowledge of the literature on the subject and inform them of existing books on the subject, or of books which you know to be in preparation. If known, full references to those works should be given, general details of their contents, and a comparison made between the existing books and the one proposed.

Q.3 *Would you recommend publication of this book?*

Notes The publisher is looking for more than Yes or No answer to this; whichever answer is given must be fully argued and justified. Many referees may find answering this difficult. However, you should bear in mind that a final decision is taken by the publisher following consultation with a number of independent referees. In short, any decision to accept or reject a proposal is a shared one.

Q.4 *Who might buy this book?*

Notes You should indicate the groups, obvious and less obvious, who might find this book of use. Identify potential primary readers, those for whom the book was obviously intended, and any secondary reader groups, those who will have some interest in it.

If possible, you should note specific nursing courses for which the book might be used as either a major text or supplementary reading.

Q.5 *What is the size of the potential readership?*

Notes Some estimate can be made of the total number of readers of this book on the following basis: If the book is suitable for use as a major text for postregistration nurses attending courses relating to the care of the elderly, all schools offering the course should be asked for their annual student intake. Similarly, if the book is directed at all staff nurses or all nursing assistants, it may be possible to establish the sizes of these two groups from existing statistical material such as that published by government departments.

When it is impossible to obtain figures for an estimate of the potential readership, this should be made known to the publisher. If an estimate is made it must be 'backed up' by the reasons for arriving at that particular figure.

Q.6 *Do you have any suggestions for improving this proposal?*

Notes Any obvious omissions from the proposal should be commented on, as should any unnecessary inclusions, publishers are *very* keen to receive well-argued and constructive criticism. If a sample chapter is included then comments can be made regarding writing style, use of references, readability and scholarship of presentation; however, these aspects will be obvious to an established publisher and are classified as opinion and not 'constructive criticism'.

Q.7 *Can you name other experts in this subject area?*

Notes The publisher may wish to use the services of additional referees, but may be unaware of the names of specialists. You should feel free to suggest the names of other potential referees who can then be approached by the publisher.

Q.8 *Are there any other points you wish to make?*

Notes Here, you should include any additional relevant comments which are not included in the questionnaire.

Q.9 *May we disclose your identity?*

Notes Some publishers may wish to disclose the identity of individual referees; most prefer to preserve anonymity. However, should they wish to disclose your name it is necessary that they obtain your permission to do so.

The preceding sample questionnaire which publishers send to referees may also be of value to those preparing a proposal for submission to a publisher. The possibility of submitting a proposal successfully is increased if the writer has a prior knowledge of the types of question which are liable to be raised by a publisher.

Having established, on the basis of a proposal and perhaps a sample chapter, that the book is required and is commercially viable, the publisher may then ask you to work on a complete manuscript. This request usually takes the form of a formal agreement or contract. When the manuscript is submitted the publisher may, in addition to having the manuscript examined by 'in house' staff, send it to one or more referees. The purpose of this second reference process is to establish that the factual content of the text is as was promised in the proposal. Remember that entering into a contract with a publisher does not guarantee that the manuscript will be published. On receiving a manuscript a publisher may seek further opinion as to the advisability of publication.

Submitted manuscripts

Although the guidelines sent to those who will referee submitted manuscripts will vary from publisher to publisher, the basic questions are similar. The explanatory notes provided after each question here are mine, not the publisher's.

Publishers do not usually ask referees to examine the grammar or typographical quality of the manuscript as these are publishing criteria and are taken care of by them; it is helpful, however, to bring misspelling of scientific terms to their attention. The referee is normally asked for a professional assessment of the content of the work, of its general readability, and whether or not the presentation is of an accepted professional level.

As publishers should not make known the name of the referee without prior permission, so they should not use the favourable comments provided by the referee for promotional or advertising purposes without written consent. If the publisher wishes to make such use of this material, the permission of the referee *must* be obtained.

QUESTIONNAIRE SENT TO MANUSCRIPT REFEREE

Q.1 *Is the work readable and interesting?*

Notes Here, the publisher is asking for the opinion of the referee in the role of an informed reader and consumer of your profession's published material. In answering this question the same criteria may be used as would apply when you are reading any other professional text.

Q.2 *Is the material accurate and well-organised?*

Notes Professional skills and knowledge are required to answer this question. Experience of using similar texts will help you to comment on whether its organisation is logical for its intended purpose. The general layout of the material in the manuscript may also be commented on although this is an area in which the editorial staff of the publisher have special expertise.

Q.3 *Is the level of the material right?*

Notes Books are invariably directed at a particular readership, students or trained nurses for example. The level at which the material is presented must coincide with its prospective readership, too low a level being as much of a problem as too high a level.

Q.4 *Is the author well-informed?*

Notes You are being asked to make a professional judgement about whether the author is well-informed in relation to the subject of the book. Obviously, your own expertise in the subject is why you were asked to referee the work.

Q.5 *Who might use this book?*

Notes The relevance of the book to professional training, whether you would recommend it, and the courses for which the book might be most suitable constitute the answer to this question.

Q.6 *Is the subject fully covered?*

Notes The extent to which the subject matter of the book is fully or inadequately dealt with must be stated. If a shift in emphasis within the book is required, this should be brought to the publisher's attention.

Prospective authors should bear the preceding six questions in mind when preparing a manuscript and try, so far as is possible, to ensure a maximum of positive comments. As with the referee's comments relating to a proposal, the decision to accept or reject never lies solely with the referee. Knowledge of this responsibility will enable a referee to make an honest and frank judgement of manuscripts.

Published books

Publishers will occasionally consult with referees regarding books which have already been published. For example, if an existing book is going into a further edition a publisher may ask one or more experts in the subject area to comment on aspects of it. Depending on the responses from the referees, the publisher may or may not make suggestions relating to changes to the author of the book. Another example of this type of consultancy occurs when a book is to be released in a country other than the one in which it was originally published. In this instance, you will need to undertake a detailed examination of the content, presentation and language of the book to determine whether changes are required prior to its release. An example of this type of work might be when a book published in and for the United States of America requires to be 'Anglicized' prior to its release on the British market.

GENERAL CONSULTANCY

A few publishers may pay one or more consultants an annual retention fee for general advice, meeting with the consultant three or four times per year to discuss new projects and to report on changes in methods and approach and subjects requiring book coverage. Such consultants are also expected to provide names and verification of abilities of potential authors and referees.

If the volume of work given to the consultant by the publisher exceeds the value of the annual payment made, then additional payments may be paid on an ad hoc basis.

JOURNAL REFEREEING

A small number of journals have a panel of referees to whom they send submitted article manuscripts prior to accepting them for publication. Although the specific remit of this type of referee may vary slightly from journal to journal, he/she is usually asked the same type of questions:

Q.1 *Does the manuscript comply with the journal's guide to contributors?*

Notes The referee will examine length, use of references and general content to ensure that the article does not conflict with requirements of the journal.

Q.2 *Is the factual material in the article accurate?*

Notes Facts such as drug doses, physiological values, related acts of Parliament and statistical material will be checked for accuracy.

Q.3 *Does the quality and general standard of the article meet the requirements of the journal?*

Notes The experience of the referee, combined with a knowledge of the general standard of the journal, will enable a judgement to be made as to the quality of the submitted manuscript.

Q.4 *Is the manuscript topical, original and up-to-date?*

Notes Here, you will rely largely on personal experience and knowledge of professional literature relating to the subject of the manuscript.

As with books, the identity of referees is confidential and revealed only with full permission of the referee. In some instances, there may be a distinct advantage in asking the author to contact the referee to discuss how the manuscript might be adjusted to meet the requirements of the journal.

Authors of submitted manuscripts should bear in mind that the job of the referee is to submit an honest and objective appraisal of the work. On receiving negative comments from a referee, the author should never try to establish or, still worse, guess the identity of the referee. A guess is liable to be wrong and can result in the destruction of friendships.

EDITORIAL PANEL MEMBER

A number of journals, headed by a member of the profession to which the journal is addressed, use the services of consultants who constitute the remainder of the editorial panel. These consultants, who may be paid or unpaid, are used for purposes which vary from journal to journal. They may act as book reviewers, article referees or may be requested to meet with the editor and the publishers periodically and discuss editorial policies and strategies relating to the journal. This arrangement ensures that a strong relationship exists between the publisher and the profession for which it publishes.

Although those journals with a large editorial staff have less need for this type of arrangement, more specialised journals with a smaller circulation depend heavily on the contribution and input of its editorial panel.

BECOMING A PUBLISHING CONSULTANT

While the type of consultants previously discussed are often recruited by publishers, there is no reason why individuals interested in becoming consultants should not get in touch with publishers and offer to make their services available. Clearly, the terms of such an arrangement would need to be fully discussed before either party made a formal commitment.

The following type of information should be included in any attempt to become involved in consultancy work. A full and detailed curriculum vitae and a clear statement of the type of consultancy work that you had in mind. For example, you might write to a journal and suggest that you be considered for membership of its panel of book reviewers. In this case, details of the specific specialist areas in which you feel competent to review books must be presented.

EXERCISES

Exercises 1—3 are designed to help you construct a proposal which could be directed to a publishing company requesting that you be considered for consultancy work. The exercises can either be used on a personal basis or form part of a writing workshop programme.

EXERCISE 1

Prepare a letter to a book publisher in which you will initiate discussions about the possibility of you working for them as a consultant. Include the following points in addition to a curriculum vitae:

Why you wish to become involved in consultancy work. Why you have chosen to offer your services to this particular publishing house. Areas of special expertise and interest. Any other relevant points.

EXERCISE 2

Select a professional text with which you are familiar and imagine it has been sent to you, in manuscript form, by a publisher. The publisher has requested that you review the enclosed manuscript and reply to the questions which have been set out on pages 153 to 154 of this chapter.

EXERCISE 3

Select any article in your subject area from a recent issue of a journal. Imagine that you are a referee for this journal and the article has been sent to you for comment. Using the questions set out on page 156 of this chapter, construct and appropriate reply to the reference request.

Chapter 14
Book Reviewing

The art of book reviewing requires many of the skills necessary for other forms of publishing, for example, the book reviewer needs a clear, concise, writing style which will convey the maximum amount of material using the minimum number of words. Most nursing journals include a section of reviews of recently published texts. Invariably these have been prepared by nurses with an expertise in the subject area of the book. My purpose is to emphasize that book reviewing should be regarded as a form of professional writing for publication, and that it is within the scope of all nurses.

WHAT ARE BOOK REVIEWS?

A book review is a critical appraisal, usually written, of a book. Books are normally sent by publishers who select journals appropriate to the subject of the book. For example, books which might have a wide professional readership will be sent to a journal which also has a wide readership. More specialised books may be sent to specialist journals *and* to wide-readership journals in the belief that the wide readership will include those to whom the book is directed.

The more specific purpose of a review is to inform the potential buyer or reader of the contents and quality of the book. Thus the review reader is relying on the credibility, credentials and expertise of the book reviewer. Being a reviewer carries with it a responsibility to the journal, to its readership and to the writer and publisher of the book.

Journals have varying requirements for the structure and length of a review; these are given to the reviewer. The requirements may range from the request to provide a review of a maximum length of 300 words, with no additional instructions; to a request to produce a 200-word review which should include a number of points contained in specific instruction to the reviewer.

In general the purpose of a review is:

To inform the reader of the purpose of that book. You must make a statement as to whether the book does what it was intended to do.

To outline and give examples of the content of the book. In some instances this might mean giving the titles of the parts and/or chapters of the work.

To describe the author or editor or contributors to the book, giving some information about their professional credentials and referring to the country or countries in which they currently work and where the book may have originated.

To include an opinion as to the quality and presentation of the contents, for example its readability, structure, grammar, references, index, appendices and whether the work is of a scholarly and professional nature.

To make a firm statement which will help the reader to decide whether to examine the book, buy one for personal use or have a copy bought for the nursing library.

Although book reviewing is a task which carries a considerable responsibility it is a rewarding, informative, and challenging means of keeping up-to-date with your specialist area and, at the same time, playing an important part in the development of nursing as a profession with its own distinct literature.

WHO COMMISSIONS BOOK REVIEWS?

In order that reviews can be impartial, unbiased and objective the reviewer works for the journal in which the review is to be published. The book publisher chooses which journals a book will be sent to for review, but the journal chooses the reviewer.

The book review editor of the journal will have a list of names of appropriately qualified individuals to whom books can be sent. For example, if a book relating to psychiatric nursing is received it will be sent to a specialist in that subject. If you feel, for any reason, that you would prefer not to review the book it should be returned to the journal with a note of explanation. For example, it may be outwith your competence, or it might be that you have personal links or friendship with the author and feel that this may prevent a wholly unbiased review. Thus you always retain the right to refuse or accept a book which you have been asked to review.

WHO WRITES BOOK REVIEWS?

The major requirement for reviewing nursing texts is that you be a professional nurse. You must be an experienced professional either in a number of areas of nursing or in a single specialist area. The experience of the potential reviewer will determine the types of book which he/she is qualified to review. For example if you have a wide experience of many areas of nursing you will probably deal with books of a general and comprehensive nature. Such a book might be one relating to the theory and application of the nursing process. Conversely if your experience is highly specialised, you may be requested to review a text such as one relating to the role of the operating theatre nurse for example. What is being indicated here is that the system requires a wide range of professional experiences and backgrounds in nurses who are to become reviewers.

Another prerequisite is that the potential book reviewer has the skill which is necessary to meet requirements of the review, and of the journal who requests it. Nurses who review books may have moved into this area of publication having previously gained experience in, for example, writing articles or books or both. However, there is no reason why book reviewing should not be a first publishing experience.

How to become a book reviewer

There are a number of ways in which nurses might become a book reviewer. First they may be contacted by a journal editor who knows them to have the necessary skill and professional expertise with which to write reviews. This type of contact, of course, is dependent on the editor knowing or having been informed of the suitability of the person concerned. This might be the case when, for example, the editor contacts a potential reviewer who is well-established and well-known for professional expertise.

Another way in which reviewers are obtained by journals, particularly new journals, is to place an advertisement in the journal inviting potential reviewers to apply. This means of recruiting reviewers, although used, is fairly rare.

The third means of becoming a reviewer depends on an initiative being taken by the person concerned, an initiative which nurses may be reluctant to take but which, nevertheless, they should be more than willing to embark on. Here, the potential reviewer writes to the journal editor and encloses a letter designed to persuade the editor to consider him/her for book reviewing.

The letter should be strong, positive and persuasive. It should contain a full description of your experience and expertise. Remember that you have something which is unique and special which you are offering to the journal. It may be of some value to enclose a carefully prepared, well-written and informative sample review of a text; one which is within your expertise. Your request may be accepted or rejected. If rejected this may be because the journal already has sufficient book reviewers in the subject area. Rejection should not discourage you, simply make a similar application to another appropriate journal.

PAYMENT OF BOOK REVIEWERS

The payment offered to reviewers by journals differs. In any event the payment is of a token nature and does not cover the full cost of time, typing cost and material. Thus book reviewing, as with many aspects of professional publishing, should be seen not as an income-generating activity but rather an opportunity to participate in the development of a literature base from which nursing can develop.

My experience of payment has been of two types. First, payment has taken the form of being able to retain the book which has been reviewed. The value of the book has been from £3 to £20. The other form has been retention of the book and a set fee.

AFTER PUBLICATION

In most instances the work of the reviewer, in relation to a particular book, ends following its publication. However, there are a number of instances in which discussion, compliment, agreement, disagreement or criticism of the review may occur. For example, I have experience and am familiar with letters to the journal relating to the contents of a previously published review. These letters may come from a number of sources, including the author of the book or from its readers. In any event book reviewers, having done their job well and without bias, have little to fear from those who might express disagreement.

WRITING A BOOK REVIEW

Although the skills required to prepare a book review are similar to those required in other areas of publishing, the potential reviewer needs some special experience in this particular form of writing.

EXERCISES

Exercises 1 and 2 are intended to facilitate the development of these skills, and can either be used on a personal basis or form part of a writing workshop programme.

EXERCISE 1

Write a letter with a maximum of 400 words, use free-flowing prose, avoid using lists and:

Give personal details including present and past work positions, professional experience and academic background. Highlight one, or perhaps two, areas in which you have special expertise. A general area of expertise might be psychiatric nursing, a more specialised area within psychiatric nursing might be psychogeriatric nursing for example.

Describe why you wish to be included on a panel of book reviewers. Reasons will include the wish to extend your writing and publishing experience, the desire to contribute more fully to the development of specialist literature, and the goal to be thoroughly aware of the specialist literature.

Describe why you wish to be placed on the book reviewing panel of that particular journal. For example, you may have a high regard for that journal generally, or you may enjoy the specialist type of material published in it. In any event it is important to inform the editor of the reason or reasons for approaching *that* journal.

Describe special background and experiences which qualify you to review books, including those which relate to the specialist area described earlier in the letter. This may include work you have had published, being a reader of the professional literature, keeping up to date by attending conferences and study days, and by being recognised as an expert. Such recognition may include invitations to speak at study days and conferences.

Finally, end with a positive statement which assumes that you have something to offer the journal, something which is unique and of considerable value. Also, assume that the letter will be viewed positively by the editor, this being reflected in the final paragraph. For example a concluding sentence might read:

'I hope that you will give this request your favourable consideration, and look forward to a continuing relationship which will be to our mutual advantage.'

EXERCISE 2

Select a nursing textbook with which you are familiar. It need not be a 'good' text, most have a number of strengths and weaknesses. Prepare a review for submission to a journal, the maximum length should be 300 words. Examine a number of published book reviews to get the feel of style, structure and content. When preparing the review refer to the suggested contents and structure on pages 159—60.

Chapter 15
Economics of Writing

Almost all writing endeavours, with the possible exception of some examination work, involves financial cost to the writer. It is true of all forms of writing dealt with in this book and, in general, can result in considerable personal financial costs. In some, although not all, instances there may be income derived from the writing which may partly or wholly offset the preparation costs. However, as soon as income is received, it becomes a subject of interest to the collectors of income tax.

Recently a student, rather apologetically, said during a discussion of professional writing opportunities 'I know this isn't a very professional question, but do writers get paid for their work?' Apart from an understandable naïveté of the economics of writing, the question was indicative of a feeling that professionalism and money do not 'mix'. My reply to the question included a discussion of the extent to which writers get paid *and* a clear indication that the question was not only 'professional' it was reasonable, indeed, essential. Thus, it is of profound importance that writers from the professions, particularly those who write for publication or in relation to some other form of commercialism, be *very* aware of its economics.

Three related topics are discussed in this chapter: writing costs, writing income and taxation. Although the discussion is not comprehensive, it will draw attention to a number of financial issues and alert you to the need to be more aware of the whole question of the economics of writing. Similarly, the discussion will *not* constitute an income tax guide, but it will alert you to some taxation implications. If in doubt about any financial points, particularly if they relate to income tax, get in touch with an accountant.

While nurses and colleagues in allied professions are unlikely to get rich by writing for publication, it is as well to keep expenditure to a minimum and to maximise income. By doing so, the possibility of not making a net loss is decreased, and the possibility of making a modest profit is increased. Although all those with whom the writer comes into contact, including publishers, are anxious to give you a 'fair deal' and to receive

value for money, the beginner needs to know some of the ground
rules to get started.

WRITING COSTS

As with many forms of expenditure, the costs of writing for
publication are often composed of a number of small sums of
money. Each outlay, in itself, seems minimal: the total cost, however, might be quite considerable and should be taken account
of when becoming involved in writing.

The items of expenditure covered in this section relate to
the range of writing activities discussed in this book. Some
items, typing for example, relate to almost all types of work
while others, indexing for example, relate only to writing a
book. You are therefore requested to be selective in your application of the material and to remember that not all items will
apply to all types of writing.

Actual costs will not be included for two reasons: First, they
will obviously vary from place to place and may depend on you
'shopping around' for the best buy. Second, costs do change over
time resulting in any amounts stated quickly going out of date.
My main purpose here is to show the type and range of costs,
rather than to describe what these may actually be.

Most of this section involves income tax implications, the difference between approved expenditure and income being the
amount on which income tax is paid. It is important that exact
details of all appropriate income and costs be kept. When
possible, *receipts* of all payments made should be kept. In addition to taxation purposes, considering the personal costs will
enable a better personal budget to be worked out and, in relation to doing consultancy work, help you to identify a reasonable
charge for the work.

Writing materials

An ample supply of good quality lined notepaper, pencils,
erasers, ruler and unlined paper for graphs are the minimum
tools for the beginner. Cellophane tape, paper clips and scissors
are useful for the frequent 'cutting and pasting' which takes
place as the work enters its various draft forms. These basic
materials are an obvious example of costs, which in themselves,

are rather insignificant. However, in addition to other expenditures they become increasingly large.

Postage and telephone

Communication costs can be quite considerable, particularly where frequent written or telephone contact has to be made with co-writers of a book or article. Postage costs are relatively easy to document, telephone costs are a little more difficult. However, the nature and purpose of each call made in relation to the writing activity should be noted along with a reasonable estimate of the cost. Postage and telephone costs arising from contact with the publisher, from 'researching' the manuscript and from obtaining permissions should also be noted. The use of stationery, packaging materials and *all* others costs associated with communicating with others should be recorded.

Typing

Many secretaries will type articles, books and other material in their spare time, charging either by the hour or by the page. An arrangement regarding typing costs should be made *before* the work is done. If the cost is per page, it must be made clear whether the cost includes any requested carbon copies, and whether charge will vary for single- or double-spacing material. Similar points should be established if work is to be done by a commercial concern. A copy of the bill or invoice should be filed with your collection of receipts.

The costs of typing materials, such as paper, carbon paper and possibly either a bought or hired typewriter, may have to be met by you. Finally, if you have not had work done by that particular typist or typing agency previously, ask for a one page sample *before* coming to a more formal arrangement.

If you do your own typing, be sure to include the cost of the typewriter, repairs, ribbons, paper, correction fluid and so on.

Binding

The costs of binding work such as dissertations and theses often relate to its length, quality, colour and the use and length of gold leaf inscriptions on the cover. You should shop around commercial binders before making a decision, the quality of work being compared with costs. If you are unsure of the quality of work done by a particular binder, ask to see a few samples.

A number of removable 'do it yourself' binders and covers are available, these may be considered as alternatives to the more permanent forms.

Artwork and photography

If photographs or art illustrations such as line drawings are required, publishers should be asked if they can provide these services, usually at a cost to the author. For example, they may have a library of photographs, or have a resident graphic artist who can produce line drawings according to your specifications. For a thesis or dissertation you should approach individuals, or organisations, such as the graphics department of a college, for help with illustrations requiring artistic skill.

If photographs need to be provided by you, it may be that those taken personally or by a good amateur will suffice. Alternatively, a professional should be asked for a quotation. Naturally, only good quality work should be paid for, and again a copy of the invoice kept for tax purposes.

Work such as line drawings may be done by a graphic artist on the basis of a payment for each drawing. Discuss your requirements with the artist and commission a single 'sample' drawing before making further arrangements. Work for publication should be discussed with the publisher before commissioning. Despite contracted arrangements, the publisher may prefer your own clearly labelled pencil roughs, but will certainly have specifications for the artist you commission.

Purchase of books and journals

All textbooks, including a dictionary, thesaurus and other professional reference books should be included in the costs of writing, particularly when a textbook is being prepared. Journal subscriptions can also be included even though not all issues will contain material of particular relevance to the current research being undertaken in relation to writing activities.

Travel

Travel, whether it be to collect material for publication or to discuss the work with the publisher or other contributors, can add considerably to writing costs. Two means of calculating this cost may be used: public transport cost or reasonable and recognised rate per mile travelled. For the former, try and obtain receipts; the latter requires your own record of mileage. Both require records of the dates and purpose of the journey.

Professional fees

If the services of an accountant are used and paid for in relation to preparing accounts for income tax purposes, then you can set payment of such a fee against income tax. The same point would apply if a lawyer is consulted in relation to a contract for example, or if a professional indexer, artist or photographer is employed.

Assistant's fees

If another person such as a professional colleague were paid a fee by you for work done on a manuscript, reviewing a book manuscript for example, this would be an additional cost to be borne in mind.

Rent, rates and heating

If you work at home, part of the cost of heating, air conditioning, rent and rates should be regarded as a writing cost. The exact amount of this tax claim (as a proportion of the total costs involved) should be discussed directly with the tax authorities, or with an accountant, first.

Indexing

Many publishers will, if required, put you in touch with a professional indexer who will prepare a book index. This contact may be direct or, more usually, via the society to which professional indexers belong. Charges made by an indexer may be based on the length of manuscript, or the length of the index.

Thus, the size and range of writing costs are not inconsiderable. They should be anticipated and recorded not only for personal budgeting purposes, they also have possible implications in relation to the payment of income tax.

WRITING INCOME

As with writing costs, the income derived from writing should be carefully recorded. The amounts of income may range from nil, as is the amount of payment for some journal articles and book reviews, to a modest income from book royalties. In some instances, publishing consultancies for example, the size of the payment received may be negotiable. These examples represent a selection of the types of income which may be obtained by authors who are nurses or members of allied professions.

Book reviewing

Payment for providing a book review varies considerably between journals, although I have never encountered one which made anything other than a very modest payment. Most journals allow you to retain the reviewed book, the value of which might range from £3 to £26, or more, at current prices. Other journals pay a modest fee, £10 for example, in addition to giving the book to you.

The time involved in reading a book for review, and of the subsequent preparation of it, are *never* paid for by financial or 'in kind' income. Perhaps the real reward is in reading the book and being able to influence the direction of professional publishing by including appropriate comments.

Articles

A few journals, particularly the more prestigious low circulation ones, do *not* pay a fee to their authors. Such journals, and some who do pay a fee, may give you a number of free reprints of the article and a copy of the issue in which the article appears.

Many journals do pay a fairly modest fee which may or may not be related to the length of the article. A typical payment for an average article might be £25–£50, a small number of high circulation journals paying considerably more. Most journals which do not pay a fee make this known; those which do may not specify the amount until the paper has been submitted, the author being offered a payment along with acceptance of the article.

In general, the payment offered to writers in professional journals is minimal and rarely enough to cover the costs. Indeed, the choice of where to submit a paper is more often influenced by the reputation of the journal than by possible financial gain.

Consultancy work

In addition to the non-nurse professionals on their staff, some medical and nursing book publishers employ suitably experienced nurses on a retainer or an ad hoc basis. Indeed, some add to the experience of their own editorial/nursing staff by 'buying in' the expertise of nurse specialists from outwith the company.

Ad hoc consultancy

Although publishers have a vested interest in maintaining good relationships with their consultants, and in paying them a reasonable fee, there is *considerable* variation in the level of fees paid. For example, I have been paid £15 to complete a piece of work for one publisher and £50 from another publisher for a near identical piece.

Although every piece of consultancy work is individual, indeed the fee may be regarded as negotiable, the following proposition is offered as a guide for publishers and their ad hoc consultants. A possible starting point for negotiation is an hourly payment equivalent to one and a half times the present gross hourly earnings (or what might be earned if he/she is not currently working) of the consultant. Thus, if the consultant has a current gross salary of £7,500, the hourly rate charged to a publisher would be:

$$\frac{£7,500 \text{ (Annual salary)} \times 1.5}{52 \text{ weeks} \times 37 \text{ hrs (Length of working week)}} = £5.85 \text{ per hour}$$

A charge of 150% of the consultant's hourly income for good quality consultancy work, bearing in mind that it may well include related telephone, postage, and typing costs, is both reasonable and appropriate. Clearly, if an individual consultant wishes to request more, that is quite appropriate providing payment is discussed with the publisher in advance of an agreement being made.

By using the type of arrangement proposed, both consultant and publisher will become much more aware of the time and effort required to undertake a particular job. It will go some way toward preventing the type of situation arising which I encountered recently in which a colleague was spending *hundreds* of hours undertaking a consultancy for which she was being paid approximately 50 pence per hour.

It is not being suggested that publishers presently underpay their consultants, or that consultants should charge unreasonable fees. Rather, it is recognised that publishers are eager to pay reasonable fees for high quality professional work. Such an arrangement might take better account of what requires to be done *and* the amount of time required to do the job.

Consultancy retainer

A second type of payment for consultancy work is the payment of an annual retention fee, £200–£400 for example. If the amount of work given to such a consultant reaches a predetermined level, additional ad hoc consultancy payments may be made.

Books

Payment for writing, or editing, a book usually takes the form of royalties, these being a specified percentage of the net or gross income from sales of the book. The manner in which royalties are calculated may also differ depending on whether the book has an author (or authors) or an editor.

Details of how royalties are to be calculated, distributed and paid should be made available by the publisher as part of the contract. Two typical examples which illustrate the payment of royalties are: first, to a sole author, and, second, to a sole editor.

AUTHOR

An author may be paid either 10% of the retail price, the published price of the work, or $12\frac{1}{2}\%$ of the wholesale price, the price paid by the bookseller to the publisher. For example, if the book sells in the bookshop for £9, 10% of the published price royalty would be 90 pence. If the bookseller pays the publisher £6 (two-thirds of the published price) for the book the royalty would be 75 pence. Although royalties may vary between publishers, or from book to book, the above example is fairly common.

The amount of royalty paid, as either a percentage of retail or wholesale prices, may be increased once a predetermined number of books have been sold. For example, the 10% figure may be increased to $12\frac{1}{2}\%$ of the retail price once a particular number of copies have been sold. There are other considerations which may be outlined in the contract such as variations in the payment of royalties on books sold overseas. Royalties are normally paid yearly with the first payment being paid on a date specified in the contract.

A number of free copies of the book, ranging from 5 to 25, may be given to the author in addition to the opportunity to buy additional copies for personal use at reduced prices.

Advance Payments

The cost of preparing a manuscript for a major textbook can be considerable, running into several hundred pounds. Because such costs might be beyond the means of many prospective authors, publishers may be approached for an advance during some point in the manuscript preparation prior to its publication. Most publishers are reluctant to pay advances in royalties, an understandable attitude bearing in mind that a large number of book proposals are started but never completed. Such advances are, if paid, deducted by the publisher from the first one, or two, royalty payments.

If you have a book proposal to which a publisher is attracted, but which cannot be written because of lack of finances, do not hesitate to request a reasonable and well-argued advance from the publisher.

GENERAL EDITOR

If one person is editing a book to which he/she and a number of other writers are contributing, an arrangement similar to the one for authors may apply. However, the distribution of royalties between the editor and contributors requires the following type of additional arrangement:

If the royalty is 10% of the published (retail) price, one third of that amount may be paid to the editor with the remainder being distributed among the contributors on a pro rata basis. If there are 20 chapters of near equal length then the writer of each chapter may receive one twentieth of two thirds of the 10% royalty. For example, if a book retails at £9 a writer contributing one chapter would receive:

$$\frac{£9 \times 10\% \times 66.6\%}{20} = 3 \text{ pence per book sold}$$

An alternative arrangement for paying contributors is to arrange a set fee, or single payment. A single, or one-off-payment, is usually calculated by an agreed figure per thousand words. The total payments on a one-off basis are generally paid by the publisher on publication and then deducted from the royalties of the general editor, after which the general editor receives all royalty income for the duration of that edition.

In either of the preceding instances, it is the general editor who determines the method of royalty division and instructs the publisher accordingly.

PUBLIC LENDING RIGHT

Under the Public Lending Right system, payment to authors whose books are lent out from public libraries is made from public funds. Information about this payment, which is *only* made if authors and books are registered, is available in relation to United Kingdom residents from: Public Lending Right Office, Rayheath House, Prince Regent Street, Stockton-on-Tees, Cleveland TS 18 1DF, England.

SERIES EDITOR

The editor of series of books might be paid royalties of 2% of total retail prices in addition to a pro rata percentage relating to his/her personal contribution.

Part of the reason for meticulous record-keeping in relation to expenditure and income relating to writing for publication is to ensure that appropriate income tax payments (neither too much nor too little) are made. Although the remainder of this chapter raises a number of issues relating to taxation, individual readers will have to ensure personally that they are aware of all rules and regulations relating to their specific circumstances.

INCOME TAX

Publishers are usually helpful in response to requests for tax advice from their authors, indeed some provide a guide for authors relating to taxation on royalties. In addition, you should feel free to seek advice from the Inland Revenue or from tax consultants. Finally, a useful and relatively worthwhile investment is in obtaining the advice of an accountant.

Articles

Profits from writing articles, or from other similar 'isolated literary activities' may be stated in a tax return by simply indicating total income *and* expenditure. For example if you are paid £30 for a successfully submitted article manuscript, the profits *may* be calculated as:

Income	Expenditure	
£30	Typing	£6.40
	Postage	£1.20
	Telephone	£0.65
	Stationery	£1.10
	Total	£9.35

Profit = £20.65

Thus, the declared net profit from that particular publication would be £20.65. Of course, it is necessary to declare gross income, then to claim for appropriate expenditure. If these details cannot be entered on the usual form, they should be placed in a covering letter or on a special form provided by the tax authorities. Of course, copies of all tax-related correspondence should be kept.

Books

Book authors may find it financially advisable to establish themselves as 'authors' for the purpose of income tax payment. The

Inland Revenue will consider, and probably grant, author status to those who have successfully published a book or who are under contract to do so. Establishing authorship status with the Inland Revenue will enable you to maximise your ability to offset appropriate expenditure against income, and to spread such expenditure over a number of years during which no income is being received.

Because of the complexity, and legal implications, of the taxation system, you are strongly advised to seek guidance on the subject from the publishers with whom you work, or from an accountant. Remember, all income and profits *must* be considered in relation to income tax, it is therefore imperative that an accurate record of all payments received be kept. Similarly, full and accurate records of all expenditure relating to writing for publication must be kept.

There is nothing 'unprofessional' about an interest in the economics of writing. Nurses and other professionals have a right, some might say an obligation, to insist on a reasonable reward in return for quality work.

EXERCISES

Exercises 1 and 2 are designed to increase awareness of varying aspects of the economics of writing, for publication or otherwise. They can either be used on a personal basis or form part of a writing workshop.

EXERCISE 1

Prepare an estimate of costs involved in preparing a 3,000-word article for publication. Assume the cost of typing the final, and possibly the penultimate, draft to be 40 pence per double-space page with an extra copy included. A double-space page of typescript may contain approximately 250 words.

EXERCISE 2

Prepare an estimate of the cost of preparing a 70,000-word manuscript for publication. Include all of the appropriate items referred to in the section of this chapter entitled 'Writing Costs'.

Epilogue

The factors which encourage professionals to go on writing beyond the point that their educational system makes it compulsory are many and varied. This is particularly true of the factors which motivate writing the publication, a difficult and yet rewarding activitiy.

As is the case with many professionals, particularly those involved with health care, nurses are motivated by a mixture of altruism and egocentricity. There can be no doubt that seeing 'your name in print' for the first time, in the form of authorship of a publication, is an extremely rewarding experience. However, the ego becomes decreasingly stimulated as more and more publishing success inevitably follows.

In the longer term, the drive to publish changes in its emphasis. Whereas, initially, ego satisfaction is *possibly* more evident than altruism, the balance reverses as experience in publishing increases. Experienced authors are often genuinely influenced by a desire to help their professional colleagues deliver a better quality of service to their patients/clients. Arguably, this desire to 'serve' is an essential ingredient of professionalism.

A modest amount of profit *may* be achieved by writing professional articles and books, particularly if attention is paid to budgeting and taxation issues. Indeed, it is important that a realistic (even commercial) approach be taken to the economics of writing. This way, contributors to the literature will be better able to continue their very necessary work.

Throughout this book, the right and responsibility of *all* professionals to contribute to their literature has been emphasised. It has been proposed that all professionals, with appropriate assistance in relation to the 'mechanism' of writing, have an important role to play. This assistance can take the form of a self-teaching programme, with possible assistance from teachers or colleagues, or a more formally structured educational experience such as may be offered during a writing workshop.

My experience with the writing-workshop approach has been positive and fruitful, with considerable advances in writing skill being achieved even in a short period. This type of

177

programme is of particular relevance to professionals who have been 'out of school' for some time and who wish to start writing for publication. I wish those who decide to learn for themselves 'Bon Voyage'. To those who decide to offer or attend a writing workshop, I suggest this book and exercises as a possible starting point.

Remember, just as a journey begins with the first step, a manuscript begins with the first word.

Recommended Reading

Alford, D.M. (1982) Editorial. *Journal of Gerontological Nursing* **8**, 198.

Binger, J.L. (1979) Writing for publication. A survey of nursing journal editors. *Journal of Nursing Administration* **9**, 50–52.

Blackwell Scientific Publications (1981) *Recommendations for Authors*. Oxford, Blackwell Scientific Publications.

British Standards Institution (1978) *Citing Publications by Bibliographical References*. London, British Standards Institution.

Butcher, J. (1980) *Typescripts, Proofs and Indexes*. Cambridge, Cambridge University Press.

Butcher, J. (1981) *Copy-editing*, 2nd ed. Cambridge, Cambridge University Press.

The Chicago Manual of Style, 13th ed. (1982). Chicago, The University of Chicago Press.

Cormack, D. ed. (1984) *The Research Process in Nursing*. Oxford, Blackwell Scientific Publications.

Hays W. (1974) *Statistics for the Social Sciences*. London, Rinehart and Winston.

Jones, J.F.A. (1978) *Taxation of Royalties: a Guide for Authors*. Oxford, Blackwell Scientific Publications.

Kirkpatrick, E.M. ed. (1983) *Chambers Twentieth Century Dictionary*. Edinburgh, Chambers.

Lloyd, S.M. ed. (1982) *Roget's Thesaurus*, new ed. Harlow, Longman.

McCloskey, J. & Swanson, E. (1982) Publishing opportunities for nurses: a comparison of 100 journals. *Image* **14**, 50–56.

Strunk, W. & White, E.B. (1979) *The Elements of Style*, 3rd ed. London, Collier Macmillan.

Trevitt, J. (1980) *Book Design*. Cambridge, Cambridge University Press.

Waldhorn, A. & Zeiger, A. (1981) *English Made Simple*. London, Heinemann.

Index